The City Slicker Chicken

and other tales

Moneca Wilson

Copyright 2003 Moneca Wilson

Spotted Cow Press Ltd.
4216 - 121 Street
Edmonton, Alberta, Canada T6J 1Y8
www.spottedcowpress.ca

National Library of Canada Cataloguing in Publication

Wilson, Moneca, 1926-
 The city slicker chicken : and other tales / Moneca Wilson.

ISBN 0-9688977-4-6

I. Title.
PS8595.I5843C57 2003   C813'.6   C2003-910730-2   PR9199.4.W54C57 2003

Printed and bound in Canada.

Printed on demand by Scan Copy Print, Edmonton, Alberta.

Designed by Melanie Eastley, some production!, Edmonton, Alberta.

Page Composition by Lu Ziola, some production!, Edmonton, Alberta.

Dedication

These tales are lovingly dedicated to my grandchildren: Christopher, Michael, Matthew, Elizabeth, Jessica, Anthony, Alexander, Jonathan and Sarah.

Acknowledgements

Thank you to the many people who encouraged and supported me in gathering together the memories from my time on the prairies.

I hope you find these tales entertaining. I hope too they convey, in some way, the noble qualities of the hard working pioneers who transformed this great plain into a thriving society.

Special thanks to Greg Neiman, Eric Wilberg, the Writers' Group, Murray Fuhrer, Joan Crate, Patricia Wynne, Pat Goulet, Sue Cockshutt, my family and friends.

Contents

Autumn

Winter

Reflection

Spring

1

A Gift from Siberia

Our springtime landscape is lovely and green. Recent rain and thunderstorms have encouraged the flowering trees and shrubs and these intersperse the green with clusters of colour – purple, burgundy, white, and pink.

The crabapple tree next door is loaded with blossoms, promising a harvest of tart red apples, which in turn translates into jars of sweet red jelly, a spoonful spreads nicely on wintertime toast.

These beautiful trees and bushes – the almond, the cherry, the lilacs – are a source of pleasure at this beginning of a new summer season. Another shrub, the caragana, is also blooming now but it elicits no exclamations of delight. It seems to be no one's choice for a showy front lawn shrub. Yet, despite its modest beauty, it could be considered a horticultural icon, having played an important role in the development of the prairies.

The hardy drought-resistant caragana, native to Siberia and Manchuria, came to Canada as the Siberian Peatree. It made its way to our western frontier with the pioneers where it

Moneca in front of Grandmother's garden

helped define our towns and farms, growing where other trees often would not grow. It was useful, too, in controlling soil erosion, especially during the drought of the 1930s.

Many settlers came from forested areas of the world and they were anxious to add the beauty and protection of trees to their piece of land. My grandparents had a fine windbreak around their farm site – trees mature enough to provide a place for nesting birds and shady paths for us children to run along. Granddad also planted trees and caragana bushes in other parts of the farm, on the leeward side of a hill, in the ravines and along the road allowances. He believed trees attracted rain.

In the small prairie town where I spent my early school years, the caragana was the most common tree, or bush, lining streets and encircling yards. In the springtime, the prickly branches sprouted a mass of small soft furry leaves. I remember pressing my face into the hedge for the tangy sweet smell of new growth and running my hand along the side as I walked by, like stroking the shiny coat of a new calf.

Soon yellow blossoms appeared. If it had been a wet spring, the caragana bloomed well, giving the bush a yellow cast. Most often though, the little flowers were scanty and we had to search for the largest ones to pick. We would nip off the neck end and taste the bit of sweet nectar. Later in the summer the seed pods, plump and shiny green, hung from the bushes. Again we had a special relationship with the caragana, perhaps a symbiotic one, for we picked the pods, opened them, scattering the seeds, and then we used the empty pods as whistles.

For some pioneers who came from the lush green English countryside, the treeless prairie demanded attention and treatment. So it was for our friends, Tom and Lucy, as they struggled on their land trying to grow a windbreak – and crops! After a number of decades of hard work with little reward, they sold out and moved into a small house in the nearby town.

Immediately, they filled their lot with trees and bushes, but it was the caraganas that responded best of all, encircling their space with a wide thick hedge. At the front gate, Tom shaped the caraganas into an arbour. It was an unusual creation and I liked to visit them just to walk under that tree arch. At Christmas time, Tom wove red and green crepe paper streamers through the arbour part of the hedge adding quite a festive touch to our small town's seasonal decoration.

I don't know how or when the caragana, alias the Siberian Peatree, arrived in our country, but it is to our advantage that it did. Tenacious and hardy, it served us well and is still being planted. Today, caragana bushes often mark the site of abandoned farm homes. When we see a cluster of them on a lonely hilltop or along a fence line, we know that at one time they were part of some family's dream.

2

March in the Midlands

March arrives in our Midlands burdened with our expectations. We expect her to release us quickly from the grip of winter and usher in a warm spring. After all, she contains the official first day of spring and that seems like a promise. But it is not always easy to oblige us; March is complex, torn by her own uncertainties and the demands of nature. She has many faces.

March is coquettish. She flirts with the winter-weary with soft caressing breezes and a swirl of summery clouds. But she is not a polished courtesan as May or June might be, and soon her other side shows – grumpy leaden skies and cold winds – that make us draw our coats closer and speak of her in critical voice.

March tries our patience. Because her disposition is uneven and her moods unpredictable, we deride her often and lament her inconsistencies. Instead, we should applaud the difficulties inherent in making the transition from winter to spring. She is obliged to rouse nature and goad it awake – not in one fell swoop, but properly in measured moves throughout the days allotted her.

I am attuned to her vagaries. On warm days, when February's snow is running in rivulets along the sidewalk, March entices the blue snow-flowers on the sunny side of the house to peek out, and pussy willow buds to appear on barren branches.

"Do not come out," I say to the swelling buds, "Stay safely in your little leather jackets. Temperamental March is not to be trusted." But they cannot resist and they burst forth, plump and furry, willing, even eager, to rendezvous with capricious March.

March may have a lingering relationship with February's winter and allows it to have one last fling – a snow storm, a cold front or a blizzard – before it is banished to the end of the year. That done, March turns to other things: blowing away the grey clouds, the snow and the lethargy in the woods and on the land.

March may be fitful and petulant, but at the end of her days the air and land will be warmer and the days longer and sunnier. Then, having run her turbulent course, she slips away, either quietly, with weariness, or with a final brief show of gusto and defiance. It is difficult to be nonchalant about March. She has a pivotal role to play as she passes through our lives each year.

3

Ain't Housecleaning Fun?

We are having a very mild winter with spring-like weather slipping in and out of our winter season. This uncommon condition may deny spring its usual privilege of announcing its official and definite arrival with a grand flourish: warm winds and melting snow banks. Usually that signaled the end of a long dreary winter and the start of spring jobs. What, I wonder, will trigger the housecleaning urge this year?

I know spring housecleaning does not have the status it once did when it was considered an annual ritual. At our farm house, after the long winter, the balmy spring weather filled Mother with a passion to throw open all windows, strip down the rooms, wash, clean, sweep, discard. We hated the chaos that created. Urgent business always took Dad to town those days. Our grumbling subsided considerably when Mother reminded us she had to take a sulphur and molasses tonic each spring when she was a child.

We started with the black soot-laden stove pipes. They were carried outside gingerly to a far corner of the yard where the soot was banged and scraped out. "What is a stove pipe?" my young grandson asked me after I told him about this chore. I tried to explain –

to someone who knows only that heat comes out of a metal register in the floor – that the lowly stove pipe provided the heat to cook food, bake bread, dry mittens, and revive chilled puppies and piglets.

The bedrooms were tackled next. All the blankets and quilts were hung outside on the clothesline and draped over fences to air in the clean spring breeze. Fortunately, the weather on major housecleaning days was always warm and sunny, but then Mother, who organized the housecleaning spree, expected full co-operation and compliance, and that included the weather.

The bedsteads were dismantled and scrubbed with soapy water and the walls, woodwork and furniture attacked mercilessly in the same way. Every item no longer of use was discarded and old clothes recycled to the machine shop or the barn to be used in mop-up jobs.

Washing the kitchen ceiling was a difficult job. Standing on a stool, I reached up with a wet cloth and scrubbed the rough plaster where the smoke from the kerosene lamp had darkened the ceiling, and the spots left by last autumn's flies and the grime over the stove. The water from the wet cloth dripped onto my face, and the pain in my neck and shoulders made it necessary to take frequent breaks or cajole another member of the family to take over. By comparison, the walls were a cinch.

We were exhausted as we prepared supper in the disorganized kitchen, then assembled the beds, bathed and fell to sleep under quilts puffed up with sweet smelling spring air.

At the very end of this two- or three-day ordeal, after everything had been washed and polished and put aright, the wooden kitchen floor was rubbed with linseed oil. Mother applied that when everyone else was in bed and during the night the pleasant, subtle aroma of the oil drifted through the house.

Thus ended a springtime ritual, ridding the home of dust and grime and winter gloom. Perhaps a positive side effect occurred at the same time, a kind of mental catharsis, clearing our minds too, of negative, confining thoughts. In any event, we all felt invigorated afterwards – without the sulphur and molasses tonic!

4

Spring – April/98

This year, Spring has had a few false starts. We had a couple of balmy weeks in January and again in February, but experience and common sense restrained me from putting away my winter boots. However, yesterday, I heard the raucous call of crows, the honking of an unseen flock of geese, and I saw two robins in the fir tree. I was thrilled to see the birds – it was like meeting old friends I hadn't seen for awhile. The season has turned; spring is back.

There is a small park across the street from my home and I walk through it and over its foot bridge on my way to the grocery store. The park is dreary, the grass brown and brittle, the trees dark and leafless. Only the pale green of the willow bushes at the creek's edge hint of things to come. By chance, while walking home one late afternoon last week, I met a young man at the far end of the bridge, a college student, who was taking photographs of the little white bridge and the creek flowing through snow-lined banks. I stopped to talk. "It is much prettier in the summertime," I felt obliged to say.

"It is lovely now," he said, "See the glint of the sun's rays on the branches and the shimmering light on the creek and in the tree tops. This is the loveliest bridge in the city," he added with enthusiasm. Well! I had forgotten how the eyes of youth perceive beauty spontaneously, how nature beckons to those who are aware.

I, too, saw things that way once upon a time – although that may have been a challenge for us who grew up on the treeless prairies. I remember, though, the landscape had its own beauty. Even the winter with its snow-wrapped fields and crimped and sculptured drifts had a unique splendour.

But it was the joyous coming of Spring that spread a cornucopia of loveliness across our land. The days warmed and little brown hilltops crept out from under their snow blankets and, almost instantly, the shy purple crocus appeared on the southern slopes. We tramped through the slushy snow to see those blossoms and to feel their furry leaves. We were forbidden to pick them.

In a farming community, the approach of Spring meant making preparations to seed the land and the garden. By mid-March, the seed catalogues were dog-eared and spindly little tomato and cabbage plants grew in soup tins lined up on window sills.

About then Granddad moved his harness "horse" into a corner of the big kitchen where he spent hours astride the bench with its upright vice-like head, sewing and repairing harness. Often the wonderful smell of leather and leather oil drifted through the house on drafts of warm air from the kitchen stove. When he wasn't using the bench, the young children climbed on and galloped across imaginary meadows.

We loved the sound of water dripping in big shiny droplets from sun-warmed roofs, to trickle down the hill. Finally, in small streams the melted snow filled the sloughs across the fields. Sometimes the small slough in the barnyard froze over during a cold snap and we were in skaters' paradise. We skated everyday after school, and at night by moonlight, flying back and forth through silvery space.

Today my feelings evoked by Spring's arrival are not as keen, tempered by my different responsibilities such as the dandelion invasion, fences in need of repair, and gutter cleaning. But now another generation – the young man on the bridge, and my grandchildren – are in my former space. That is a comforting thought.

5

The Family's Pet Beetle

My daughter and her husband are thinking of buying a new Volkswagen car – the model that was reintroduced into Canada in 1998.

The new car, still often called the Beetle, is a classy-looking number – a refined version of the one Granddad drove 48 years ago. His car served him well and, although it suffered certain indignities and some abuse, it proved to be truly a "people" or family car.

Motorized transportation and tractors were a godsend to the pioneers and accelerated the development of the Prairies. Until he acquired the Volkswagen, Granddad drove a 1928 Ford truck, shiny new when he bought it and a great help in his bricklaying business.

There was much demand for his work from the new settlers. The little truck took him over dirt roads and muddy trails to farmsteads far and wide where he plastered a new frame house or laid down a cement sidewalk in a growing hamlet or village.

The truck required minimal upkeep; but one year, he had the motor overhauled at a local garage. He was chuckling when he brought the truck home. After the mechanic had put the motor back together, there was one piece left over and Granddad had that in his hand. The vehicle continued to run well for many more years. I wonder if Henry Ford ever realized that there was one superfluous part in his cars' motors.

The old truck retired when Granddad did – or perhaps it was the other way around. Then he, a man of frugal nature, splurged and bought a new car, a Volkswagen, in the early 1950s, just after they were first imported into Canada. The Beetle population grew over the next few years and soon there was one in many driveways and farmyards.

Granddad had to make a few changes to the body to meet Canadian standards. The rear window had to be enlarged and new signal lights installed to replace the little bars that flipped out as direction indicators.

The car cost around $700 back then, and provided immeasurable pleasure for my grandparents for many years as they cruised the countryside, up and down prairie roads with frequent trips to our farm.

When Granddad died, the Volkswagen became the property of his son, my Uncle Hubert. He lived in the city, and although he was in his 40s then, he had never owned a car.

Uncle Hubert was a big man, but he folded himself into the front seat and learned to drive. He never mastered the gear shift located on the floor and the car was always driven in second gear so the take-off was uneven and jerky. Over the years, that caused his wife some neck problems and other drivers consternation, especially at green lights. Each spring, he would often drive into the country and, on rainy days, the Beetle became mired on some unpaved road.

"Stupid people!" he would rail, "They build the car too low, too low." And, again, some patient farmer would come with his tractor and pull the car out.

After some years, Uncle Hubert bought a new car, an automatic, and the Beetle was handed down to me. It was great to have it to scoot around in but, because of the delicate condition of the gear box, I did not venture far afield. It was like a family pet by then, with its bumps and scratches and cockeyed front bumper.

One day, a big brute of a car, comparatively speaking, plowed into the back and along with other repairs, our Volkswagen needed a paint job. We decided to break with the traditional nondescript beige and paint it bright blue. For some reason, the sun had a bad effect on that colour and faded it in spots so that we soon had a unique, blotchy, psychedelic-coloured car.

My teenage kids thought the car was neat, cool and groovy. When it was their turn to learn to drive, the Volkswagen served that purpose well. They had no trouble with the gear shift, which had been replaced by then, so earned their licenses without a problem. They became the fourth generation in the family to drive Granddad's Beetle.

In a few years, the kids had their own second-hand cars and our Beetle, weary and battered, and in need of major repairs, was retired to a shady spot in our city backyard, set up on blocks to await further development. The following year, a connoisseur of old Volkswagens bought the car and towed it away. We watched it go with much regret.

The Volkswagen isn't associated with the opening of the prairies as is, for instance, the Model T Ford, but with its stoic dependability, it provided useful service as prairie development moved into another phase after the war.

It is good to see it back in style, like bell-bottom jeans and platform shoes. I hope my daughter and her husband buy the car and I'll get to ride in one again. Not only that, their children, Elizabeth and Jonathan, will also be treated to the Beetle experience.

6

The Rains Came Too Late for Mr. Jacob

Farming is not an easy business. We hear about the difficult conditions facing the farming community these years; sometimes the problems are complex and the solutions elusive. I can empathize with those affected, as I remember my father and his contemporaries struggling against great odds during the drought years decades ago, when despair was the prevalent mood in the land.

Farmers then were a tenacious bunch, committed to their farms and community. In time, when the drought broke, there were productive years, and Dad and his neighbours thrived. But that was not the outcome for all who toiled on the land; some fell by the wayside due to circumstances beyond their control.

One such person was Mr. Jacob. I did not know him personally, but his sad story was often talked about. Then too, our entire community suffered some long term communal guilt about his unhappy end.

My uncle had taken a particular interest in Mr. Jacob, whom he got to know well when he worked in the bank in the small prairie town. Mr. Jacob's last name had many Zs and Ks, so he asked people to call him by his first name. He was a quiet, gentle man and the bank staff liked him. Mr. Jacob was especially fond of my uncle who also had Zs and Ks in his name, and sometimes they spoke a bit of Polish to one another.

He told Uncle about Anna, his betrothed in the old country, who was waiting for him to come back to marry her and bring her to Canada. One day, in early summer, he made another deposit, pulling out a bank book and a grain ticket from the pocket in his flannelette shirt, behind the bib of his overalls. He told my uncle he was soon going for Anna.

Weather conditions changed then, and the cycle of dry years began. Mr. Jacob did not make any more deposits; instead he had to withdraw money. On his infrequent visits to the bank, he spoke little and never about his dream of Anna. Each spring he seeded, but the drought was relentless and in the autumn there was disappointment again.

One dreary March morning, Mr. Jacob walked out to the barn and opened wide the barn door. He untied the two skinny horses and waved them out. He did the same to the cattle – the old milk cow, the heifer big with calf, and the gangly steer he had hoped to fatten for market. Then he sat down in an empty stall and leaned over the barrel of his gun.

It was four days before his body was found. The old milk cow, had managed to walk the four miles to the main road. A farmer on his way to town saw the dead animal in the road allowance and wondered.

In mid-afternoon the young constable and the doctor arrived at Mr. Jacob's farm. In the course of examining him, they found in the breast pocket of his shirt, under the bib of his overalls, a few bits of paper and an old worn bank book. It showed a balance of 82 cents. It was really more than a tattered old bank book: it was the story of one man's life and dreams and final despair.

7

The City Slicker Chicken

When I was reading the fable of the City Mouse and the Country Mouse to my young grandson the other day, it brought to mind the Saga of the City Slicker Chickens. It is a tale we often tell around the family table, one that originated and unfolded in our city home a number of years ago when we became the recipients of a couple of four-day-old chicks. With their arrival came some interesting experiences – and havoc!

That Easter season the teenage son in the family next door gave his baby brother two fluffy chicks. Little Andy was delighted and miraculously did not squeeze them to death.

Fortunately, from the chicks' point of view, my eight-year-old daughter overheard Andy's mother lament that there was absolutely nothing she could do but send them to the SPCA or, even worse, subject them to a fate more dreadful than that. Rumour had it she once flushed a goldfish down the toilet.

Joanne came flying into the kitchen sobbing this news to me.

"Can we take the baby chicks, Mother?" she pleaded. "Can we, can we?"

I was not surprised by her concern. Joanne felt an affinity for every living creature and was in the habit of befriending, adopting or abducting any willing animal from a mouse to a St. Bernard dog. At least this time she was asking permission first.

I pointed out the disadvantages. We did not have a backyard fenced with chicken wire, and Toby, our small dog of mixed ancestry, might not take kindly to the chicks and could dispatch them easily in one small gulp.

As usual, Joanne persisted and the two baby chicks joined our menagerie. With a wooden apple box and some netting from an old crinoline, she constructed a shelter in the backyard. It became, almost immediately, inadequate at containing them.

To our surprise, Toby took an intense interest in the chicks, not as hors d'oeuvres but as creatures in need of mothering. Maternal instincts raged through her little body and she literally adopted the baby chicks, lavishing constant attention on them. She followed them around nudging them back when she thought they had gone too far astray and gathering them with her paws into her furry tummy to sleep.

As the chicks grew they seemed to develop split personalities. Small wonder! Should they bond with Toby or Joanne or heed their inherent nature? One day when Toby was barking at a startled mailman, the two chicks, now robust at five weeks old, stood behind the dog cackling furiously. Gradually, they became more adventurous, scurrying about the yard, the front road, the alley, and into neighbours' gardens. Toby was worn to a frazzle trying to control them. Clearly things were getting out of hand.

Fortunately, a solution presented itself. Grandmother and Granddad came to visit. They lived on a farm and had an empty chicken coop so our two adoptees travelled back with them. Toby grieved for the chickens and slept in the empty apple box for a few nights. Joanne's anguish was eased by Grandmother's other solemn promise to never, ever roast or pan fry the chickens.

The gangly, squawking birds grew fat in the farmyard among the grass and abundant supply of worms. However, one morning when Grandmother was feeding them one of the chickens choked on the food and fell dead at her feet. She felt sad as she buried the bird in the soft ground behind the chicken coop.

The remaining chicken flourished and grew into a handsome young cock with long feathers that shone green and orange in the sunlight. He was a high stepper with well-rounded thighs and a firm broad breast.

But Grandmother remembered her promise to Joanne. When the rooster's relationship with the magpies in the farmyard seemed about to degenerate into more than name-calling, she decided to find a new home for him. He was moved to the neighbour's farm where he joined their big healthy flock and soon established a lofty position in the pecking order.

He was quite pompous and spent his days strutting about, regaling the admiring flock with tales of life when he was a city slicker chicken. The surroundings were to his liking and the food was good. From a rather uncertain beginning, no doubt his universe unfolded as it should.

8

The Man Who Loved Trees

During the month of May, we celebrated several important events: May Day, Victoria Day, Mother's Day. I especially enjoyed the latter and the pampering that went with it. But May contains another special day that is not as well known, not even observed, it seems. Yet I believe its intent and purpose surpass all the others in importance and real relevance to our current society and to our future on the planet. I am referring to Arbor Day.

We observed Arbor Day on May 5 when I was growing up on the farm, although the date seemed to vary across the country. Despite the lack of exuberant celebrations, then or now, that day and its meaning are firmly entrenched in my psyche. I grieve when a tree is cut down and apologize to each dandelion as I dig it out of my lawn.

Much of this strong sense of connection to growing things is due to Mr. Myer's influence. He is the teacher I had for most of my elementary school years, and his reverence for nature impacted on all his students. Because of him, I have fourteen trees crammed onto my small lot in the city.

Mr. Myers was an environmentalist before the word was coined, or at least before such advocacy was popular. He may not have known, or cared, about the historical beginning of Arbor Day in 1872, but the principles it preached, "tree planting for the beautification of towns, the importance of forest preservation, etc." were dear to his heart.

His love of the outdoors and growing things was ingrained growing up in the rolling, forested hills of Caledonia, Ontario. As a young man, he came west to teach at a country school, and he was dismayed to find nary a tree – nothing to break the wide sweep of prairie land stretching to every horizon. All he could find were a few saskatoon and willow bushes growing in the coulees folded into the land here and there.

Mr. Myers taught the robust farm children well. But he soon had another objective in mind: to change the landscape by planting trees. He enlisted support and aid from his students and we were eager to help, enticed by our own vision of stately woods, green and shady.

Quiet amusement was the response from parents. I told my Father about our plan to transform our bald prairie. "So," he said, with a twinkle in his eye, "good idea!" Though the adults were skeptical, none discouraged us nor criticized our teacher's extracurricular activity. They, I thought, would also love a woodland filled with flowers and birds.

At the beginning of May, around Arbor Day, Mr. Myers drove to the railroad station in the nearest town, loaded the bundles of tree plantings he had ordered into the rumble seat of his old coupe and brought them home to his teacherage. The school trustees told us to plant the trees in a row or two along the perimeter of the schoolyard – whereupon my dream forest shrunk considerably!

When the wrapped bundles of trees were opened I was disappointed again – they were not miniature maples, but foot-long twigs or sticks called cuttings.

"These will be caragana, maple and poplar trees," Mr. Myers explained to his perplexed students.

For the next few weeks we faithfully watered the planted sticks, though doubtful by then about the entire operation. Soon, however, little leaves sprouted miraculously on the seemingly dead wood.

Mr. Myers tended the rows well and when he was away on summer vacation he paid Joey, one of the students, to do the same. Most of the trees survived and we took pride in our fledgling hedge. In a few years, by crouching down, we could even sit in its shade and eat our lunch.

Over the next half dozen years, before he married and moved away, Mr. Myers planted more "sticks" around the countryside, some in low spots along dusty roads, where eventually patches of greenery graced the roadside. At the same time, farmers in the area decided to try their hand at growing trees as well as wheat, and windbreaks arose around most farmyards.

Mr. Myers, by example, promoted the tenets of Arbor Day. The old school house where he fostered our environmental movement is long gone, but our rows of trees are still standing. And, yes, birds do build nests in their beautiful branches.

The City Slicker Chicken and other tales

Summer

9

An Architectural Icon of the Prairie

Anyone who grew up on the prairies harbours a fondness for the tall, slender grain elevators. They anchor the little villages gathered at their base and, years ago, were beacons of community to isolated and lonely homesteaders.

There is, however, another building which played an important role and rightfully deserves our homage. Modest in size and not endowed with the romantic aura of the elevator, these structures were indispensable to the residents of town and country. I am referring, of course, to that wee house of the prairies, the backhouse.

We prairie dwellers cannot claim to be the architects of this structure, but I believe it is here that the humble outhouse reached a new height in numbers and design, elegance and diversity of use.

The arrival of the pioneers and the appearance of these buildings was simultaneous. My grandparents lived in a sod house for the first few years on their homestead and I wondered what toilet facilities they had. After some investigation, and my interrogation of an ancient uncle, I learned just how their first backhouse had been constructed.

Uncle Ollie told me that a rectangular hole had been dug back into the side of a hill, thus creating three earthen walls. A sod roof was placed on top, poplar poles formed the seat, and a canvas flap covered the door. That was an ingenious method and certainly environmentally friendly and thus, deserves noting here for posterity. Later the same technique was used to build a root cellar. In a different spot!

As the years went by, Granddad's backhouse evolved until, by the time I arrived on the scene, it was a solidly-built two-seater set in a sandy poplar grove in the backyard. Painted white and green to match the new house, it had a gable roof, a screened ventilator and a seat scrubbed satin smooth by an overly zealous aunt. All spiders and flies were mercilessly swept out by the same person, so it was not an unpleasant place to be on a summer day leafing through an old Eaton's catalogue. When the catalogue was placed in the backhouse, its end was imminent; toilet paper as we know it was nonexistent then. The bolt on the outside of the door was strong and firm, a fact well proven the day my brother and I locked the hired man inside.

On my father's farm, the outhouse, or john (it had many names), sat discreetly behind some lilac bushes. We painted it pink inside and lined the walls with pinup pictures of movie stars. In time, when its purpose changed, Mother stored her garden fertilizer there and an old engine from the pump jack.

The neighbour's backhouse held up a pile of firewood, or vice versa, and it anchored one end of the clothesline. Crumbs were laid on its lean-to roof for the birds in the winter, and in the summer the roof was an occasional refuge for the mother turkey to rest away from her large brood.

Spurred by a sense of mission to further research this fascinating subject, I travelled to my grandparents' deserted homestead last summer. Most of the buildings had crumpled, the barn was door-less and sway-backed, and the windows in the old faded house broken and open to pigeons. But in the back, still sheltered by a gnarled poplar, the backhouse stood intact, sturdy and upright, the rusted bolt still holding the door in place. There was an example of fine craftsmanship applied to a building deemed worthy of the very best!

Not all these buildings have had such staying power; they were neglected and shunned when the arrival of indoor plumbing made their purpose redundant. Since then, the grand old prairie backhouse has been quickly, even eagerly, forgotten. But, in their time, they were as much a fixture of prairie life as the exalted grain elevators, and deserve equal reverence.

10

The School House

We often take a drive through Alberta parkland in the summertime to enjoy the beautiful scenery and to search out winding creeks and roadside parks. A few weeks ago we had an extra reward when we came upon a relic from a past era – a one-room country school house. It was faded and boarded up, tucked with its few companion bushes into a corner of a wheat field. It looked neglected, but at least it hadn't been demolished, a fate that has befallen most of its kind.

Many years ago those modest buildings were the seats of learning and the centres for cultural activities, such as Christmas concerts and Valentine's Day celebrations. Social events, card parties and dances were held there. The dances brought together all the residents of the area for a rare opportunity to mingle and have fun! I have great memories of a dance I attended one winter when I was old enough to stay awake all evening and enjoy the sights and sounds of the event.

As was the custom in those days, the entire family went; children were not excluded from the excitement and baby sitting was unheard of. Soon after dark, the small school house quickly filled with farm folks. There was much commotion and hilarity as old friends greeted one another, the women exclaiming loudly about the growth and breadth of children. The men gathered at the back and discussed politics, a topic of perpetual importance to the depression and drought-weary farmers.

In one corner, two fiddlers and a guitar player tuned up – a discordant prelude to the sweet music we were about to enjoy. My opinion, however, in this regard is unreliable as I have no musical ability. Mother told me when I was three years old that I had a "tin ear" and it wasn't until some years later I realized, happily, that I was not partly robotic.

The school house was lit by a hissing mantle lamp hung from the ceiling. In the glare of its white light the women looked pale with stiffly curled hair and rouged lips. The men, in general, were ruddy faced due to their outdoor vocation. The children sat together on the benches and desks pushed back against the walls and watched wide-eyed as their parents swirled or laboured around the dance floor. As the evening wore on, many of the youngsters climbed upon the pile of coats at the back and fell asleep.

Our most distinguished resident – by virtue of his claim to nobility – was at the gathering with his family. It was generally accepted the man had a peerage, but I remember being disappointed to see nothing in his demeanor to indicate royal birth. He looked much like the other men in the room, though portly, with suspendered pants pulled high over his ample waist.

His lordship had married a local girl, plain and prolific. She was stooped with labour rather than age. Once she had stashed away the children hovering around her skirt, she and her husband took to dancing with great vigour. He did, in what may be considered a courtly manner, eventually ask every woman present to dance, making no distinction as to girth or gait.

The wiry, grey-haired fiddlers showed no signs of weariness and continued to saw out tunes – *Turkey in the Straw* and *The Tennessee Waltz* – until the dancers finally tired. The *Home Waltz* signalled the end.

The moon hung low in the western sky as the subdued revellers and their sleepy children piled into sleighs and headed home. We sat on the straw in the bottom of the sleigh box, warm blankets pulled up to our chins. The strains of a waltz rang in my head, echoed by the sound of steel runners on hard snow. I saw the light fade in the school house windows as the mantle lamp was turned off. The place had until Monday morning to regain the demeanor and dignity of a classroom.

I am glad that the little school house we saw last week is still standing – it is a meaningful part of our heritage. As we drove away, down the country road, I found myself humming *The Tennessee Waltz*. Off-key, of course.

11

Granddad was a
Different Kind of Pioneer

Most western Canadians can count one or two pioneer ancestors on their family tree. Often such ancestors were farmers or homesteaders. But not always: many were pioneers in other fields such as the professions, merchandising, and construction, and they too faced formidable challenges and made great contributions to our country.

Such was the case with my granddad, who came to Canada in 1911 and spent a long life in the construction trade. In the old country where he grew up, all young men were required to serve two years in the army, and while doing so they were also taught a trade. Granddad chose stone masonry. When he finished his military stint, he still had two more years of training in his trade ahead of him.

During those apprenticeship days, he studied all aspects of stone masonry with the most respected artisans in the trade. He worked on big and small projects. He learned to contour and pile stones to reflect the flow and purpose of the work, whether it was a squat rambling stone fence or the upward sweep of a lofty spire, how to "feel" the stone and to cut it so as to reveal the grain and beauty of the piece, much as a sculptor would do. At the end of his long apprenticeship he proudly became a Master stonemason.

When Granddad came to Canada he brought along old manuals of design and instruction, which we children were privy to, when we were sick in bed, that showed pictures of stone houses, some incorporating wooden beams, and diagrams for window casings, spires and gothic arches. It was his intention to continue to do similar work in his new country.

But there was little call for his line of work on the prairies then; expediency in construction generally took precedence over artistry in form. This reality forced him to put his aspirations on hold, and he turned to plastering and stucco work. In the area around the small town where his family settled after leaving the city, that work was in demand, as homesteaders moved from their first small shacks into more substantial houses. So, for years, Granddad had to settle for spreading mortar on walls instead of doing the stonework he had worked so hard to learn.

Then, in the late 1940s, he was provided the opportunity to use his master talents. He was hired to do the stonework on a new church. As this was the work he loved to do, he applied himself with great diligence and devotion, happy to be part of such a significant project. Every Sunday, after the supper meal, we all walked up the hill to observe the construction and Granddad would explain what aspect of the structure was taking form that week.

The construction took an entire summer of hard labour, cutting and placing hundreds or thousands of stones. When finished, his craftsmanship, and that of others, produced a beautiful fieldstone church of neo-gothic design with magnificent buttresses. He was proud of the building (as were all the town folks) and he considered it a monument to the work he rightfully viewed as an art form.

I wish I could say the church is standing yet, admired still by all who pass that way. But such is not the case. A larger edifice was needed and, despite protests, that unique building was smashed to the ground. I am glad that didn't happen until after Granddad's death.

Still standing though, are the two stone pillars he built at the entrance to the town cemetery. I wonder, as he laboured there, when he was well past his prime, if he had mused about the day he would pass through that entrance to his final resting place on the hillside amongst his old friends. For, after a long productive life, that is how it ended for my pioneer granddad.

12

A Journey of Considerable Pleasure

By the time the Great Depression swept over the world in the 1930s, prairie residents were already facing major problems. They were battered, not only by the grim economy, but also by a relentless drought that had a dreadful effect on the land and the people. The worldwide economic upheaval seemed remote to them. What did the price of wheat matter when there was none to sell?

At that time, the perimeter of our world was quite small, defined by the distances easily reached by horse and buggy. That area encompassed a school, a small hamlet, a church and all the farm homes in between. A trip to the big town, 20 miles away, was considered an excursion to the outside. Only occasionally was such a journey necessary.

One day in July, Father needed a special part for the cultivator. Mother and Auntie were to make the trip to town and it was my turn to go along. A dream come true, the highlight of the summer!

We left the farm early in the morning when the air was still fresh and cool, though the cloudless sky promised another hot day. With Auntie holding the reins, Queenie, our big farm horse, pulled the buggy out the gate and we were on our way.

Mother and Auntie sat on the one seat with a sealer of coffee and a bag of sandwiches at their feet. I stood in the back, behind the seat, on the bundle of oats that was Queenie's lunch. Sometimes I sat down on the bundle, my back against the seat, and dangled my legs over the edge where the dust, raised by the buggy wheels, settled on my white socks. There was much idle chatter and laughter; a one-day vacation from daily toil was a rare treat.

Queenie trotted stoically along the road that in some places was merely a trail through wheat fields and parched pasture land. Half-way to town we stopped at an abandoned farm site. While Queenie rested, Mother, Auntie and I wandered around the piece of prairie that had once been a farmyard. The house had been pulled down, but a few trees and bushes still grew around crumbling foundations. We looked there for berries or a relic, and wondered aloud about the folks who had once lived there. They had been friends of Grandmother, and neighbours to others. But adverse conditions overcame them and one spring they packed their belongings into a horse-drawn wagon and, with another family, trekked north to the Peace River country.

When we arrived in town, we tethered the horse in a shaded spot in the alley behind Granddad's house. Then we walked up and down main street, savouring the variety and interesting sights of such a cosmopolitan place. We browsed through the shops – the grocery store with its countless items and many smells, and the hardware-harness place. We lingered in the drug store, where the shiny bottles of cosmetics and perfumes stood in a row. Afterwards, we sat in the cool interior of the Chinese restaurant and enjoyed an ice-cream cone. Mother had already purchased the part Dad needed and a bag of peppermint candies for the children at home.

We headed back in the early evening when the heat of the day had abated. I sat quietly on the front seat, squeezed between Mother and Auntie, and reflected on the events of a

Tilling the new land (2 horsepower)

perfect day. Queenie's homeward gait was quick and steady and we pulled into our farmyard as the long summer day was ending.

The conditions wrought by the Great Depression and the drought fostered a somewhat narrow and parochial view of my world. But, as you see, life was not without meaning or value, nor without pleasurable events. A one-day excursion to the nearby town was one of those events – a break from routine and a stroll through another world, one we didn't get to visit very often.

13

Canning is a Work of Art

Midsummer is berry-picking time. My primordial hunting-gathering instinct kicks in, and I want to head for the hillsides with an old ice-cream bucket in hand.

This instinct was well nurtured in my youth. Our entire family participated in what was, in those days, a common event: several journeys each summer by horse and buggy to the Sand Hills in search of saskatoons and chokecherries. That area, about 15 miles south of our farm, was an uninhabited stretch of tree-covered, rolling land. Rumour had it that strange animals lived there, and one rancher who hated people, especially children my age.

In those depression and war years, summer camp or a trip to the mountains was out of the question, so an all-day jaunt to the distant berry patch was the highlight of our school vacation. It also provided us with adventures that grew in significance with the retelling over the winter months.

On berry picking day, we left home at the crack of dawn, our horse-drawn buggy loaded with sandwiches, coffee, pails, and even a wash tub, in anticipation of a profitable trip. Since there were six children in the family, we took turns going with either Mother or Dad.

Sometimes we went with our neighbour Mr. Jake and his wife Katie, in their big Bennett buggy. A trip with them usually turned into a jolly picnic with few berries to show at day's end. Mr. Jake was a big man with hulking shoulders and a perpetual smile. He entertained us with silly jokes and songs as we drove around exploring the area. More frequently than necessary, we stopped at some vantage point – on the top of a small round hill where the grass was brown and brittle and the view wonderful, or under the trees at the edge of a murky slough where we ate our bologna sandwiches.

By the end of the season we always had at least one tub full of saskatoons. We enjoyed them in muffins and pies, but they were most delicious uncooked, piled in little berry bowls and covered with thick cream and sprinkled with a few granules of sparkling sugar.

Those tasty desserts were incentives to keep us involved in the tedious task of preparing and preserving the fruit. All members of the family were commandeered for the "picking over" phase – except Dad, as urgent business took him to town on those days. Bent over the tub of berries, we scooped up a handful and as we picked out twigs, leaves and dried berries, the good ones trickled through our fingers into another pail. Soon my hands, and the chubby little hands of my younger sisters, were stained purple. And our mouths, too, though soon we had enough tasting and even the biggest and juiciest berry did not tempt us.

After the berries were washed in the water we lugged in from the pump and warmed on the stove, they were packed, with hot syrup, into glass jars and placed in the big copper boiler filled with water. Though the day was likely to be hot and sunny, we kept the fire stoked and the water boiling for about an hour. Then Mother, flushed with triumph and heat, removed the steaming jars filled with purple fruit and placed them upside down on the kitchen table to cool and to be admired.

In due course the saskatoons were canned, the chokecherries made into jelly and all the jars filed away on shelves in the cool earth-walled basement. Mother made at least one hundred quarts of saskatoon preserves, and often she would announce that great accomplishment to her neighbours. However, one lady, without fail, and without burden of proof, insisted on topping her count, and that banter provided us with a chuckle.

Nevertheless, the sense of accomplishment in creating an edible work of art and providing nourishing food for her family gave Mother a feeling of pleasure and happiness. Canning was a ritual that happened every summer and autumn and grounded and connected us with reality and the source. Perhaps that point is missed today when we pick up a jar of jam at the supermarket.

In those years, when the family gathered around the big kitchen table for the evening meal, the food was often bland and unvaried. But, when we had a dish of succulent berries swimming in rich purple juice from Mother's basement lode, we did not envy the repast of a king.

"The old house" visited by great and great-great grandsons (July 1998)

14

The Lost Village

It's not down on any map

True places never are.

– Herman Melville

My grandson Chris is brimful of teenage wisdom. The other day he tossed an old adage at me: " If a tree falls in the forest and no one is there," he said, "does it make a sound?"

"Well…," I stalled.

"Reality is relative," he pronounced emphatically.

I was not about to challenge him on any point. After all, he is sixteen and knows everything. Strangely though, because of a recent trip to the place of my childhood, his statement struck a chord. That trip left me unsettled, wondering about the interplay between imagination, dreams and facts. It caused me to question the mode of my early life.

When I was growing up there on a prairie farm in a corner of western Saskatchewan, I was very familiar with the countryside in our area – the hills, the coulees, the trails – and I knew all our neighbours since we lived in a small, closely-knit community. That was my lifestyle then and it remains entrenched in my memory.

I clearly remember the trips by horse and buggy made with my grandmother to the nearest village. The purpose of those jaunts was to exchange a crate of fresh eggs at the store for one or two dollars' worth of groceries.

We left the farm early in the summer mornings, before the heat in those cloudless drought years made the trip uncomfortable for us and for Flip, the buggy horse. We went out the east lane through a little coulee where saskatoon bushes grew, then onto the main road.

Travelling down the east hill we passed our neighbours' farms. The Wolskys lived on the right-hand side of the road. Their small unpainted house was home to ten children. Half of them came out to wave as we went by. Further along, on the other side of the road, lived the bachelor, Benson, reputed to hate children my age.

Flip, looking neither left nor right, trotted the three miles along the dusty road, across the railroad tracks and into the little village. It consisted of two elevators, one store, a post office and four small houses with poplar trees growing in their backyards.

Grandmother conducted her business in the gloomy store. It was crammed with boxes and bags and all sorts of items on the shelves and stacked on the floor. The air was filled with a mix of smells – oil and licorice and coffee – certainly different from the lysol smell which often flavoured the air in my grandmother's house. The proprietor, I remember, was pleasant and always enquired after Grandmother's health and the condition of the crops. She was not one given to unnecessary chatter, so our stay was brief.

We walked next door to the small grey post office building. A few marigolds and pansies grew in the dry earth at the entrance. The post-mistress, Mrs. Jenny, was a widow and a farmer. She was tall with a tired face and faded red hair piled loosely on the top of her head. She and her husband had come from Ontario decades before to homestead a piece of prairie. Mrs. Jenny still clung to that land because she felt, as my grandmother did, there was nothing else to do in those hard times.

When I returned to that area after being away for years, I walked through the wheat fields and found Grandmother's farmyard. The site had been abandoned decades before, but the dilapidated old house remained. From the east hill I was dismayed to see that the countryside appeared empty. Not only had the Wolskys and Bensons moved away, but even their farm sites had disappeared, lost now in the wide grain fields.

The road Grandmother and I used to travel was now only a tractor trail. I followed it in my little car over the grass and thistles growing where the railroad used to be to the spot that was once the village site. The village had vanished too. Completely. The elevators and the buildings and the paths made by young feet on their way to school were all gone. And the poplar trees. What happened to the trees? I searched, but there was nothing, not even a stone to mark its place.

I stood in the emptiness, surrounded by the sweeping prairie land, and wondered what had happened to the place and to the familiar people who had lived there. Where did they go? Based on the apparent evidence, the village had never been a reality. Was my recollection of a past life in error, having form only in my mind? Perhaps my grandson has a point.

The silence, oppressive in the summer heat, hummed in my ears and I felt that if I stayed very long, I might vanish too. I went back to my car.

The City Slicker Chicken and other tales

15

I Remember West Valley

The headlines in the weekly farm magazine screamed at me: "Farm Family Exodus Continues." The article went on to say that "hundreds of families leave the farm each year." For someone, such as I, who grew up on a prairie farm, a statement like that strikes a responsive chord and conjures up a vision of empty houses and a melancholy landscape.

A few years ago, I returned to visit Dad's old homestead in what I call "West Valley" in eastern Alberta, and there I saw the physical evidence of the exodus. The area was void of human habitation.

I ignore the expert's explanations and pronouncements and search my mind and heart for the reason. Many years ago, in West Valley, it seemed that all the necessary elements were present to support a stable, permanent community; but, like some little kingdom, it rose and flourished and fell in the span of a lifetime. Why did that happen? What factors were missing or misused? Were economics the sole cause of the community's demise? Within the history of our valley some clues must lurk.

The foundation for the development of the prairies was ably laid by courageous and hard-working men and women who arrived from other parts of the country or from other parts of the world. Facing the elements, and their fears, they wrestled the vast lands into a new order, creating communities of villages or towns with homes, roads, schools, stores and other services and, sometimes, hospitals. In such a manner, the country was fashioned and the character of the society moulded.

West Valley was part of this agricultural order by 1930. Then each quarter-section or half-section of land boasted a farmhouse, a barn and a clutter of out-buildings surrounded by a windbreak of trees.

As a young child, I was not fully aware of the dreadful effect the drought and depression had on my parents and neighbours. I do remember the dust-laden wind, the grit in my teeth, and Mother putting damp towels on window sills to keep the dust out of the house. Mounds of sand piled along the fences and in the garden where we children built tunnels and roads. There was a time for fun: church picnics, school concerts, and long evenings of cribbage and Norwegian whist huddled over by Dad and his friends talking politics. Strong self-reliance sustained these people through the devastating 1930s and at the end of the decade they were all still firmly entrenched in West Valley.

In the next decade, the rains returned and it was a time of rebirth for the area and for the weary, wasted residents. The change began one late spring day in 1939. A familiar, huge, black cloud moved towards us in ominous silence and when it engulfed our farmyard, instead of howling wind and whipping dust, rain, volumes of rain, fell. Dad went outside and stood in the rain and soon was drenched to the skin. Mother smiled at his "silliness" and we children sensed that something very special had happened.

The land bloomed. Everything turned green: the fields, the pastures, the gardens. Life, in general, improved and activity settled into a vibrant and happier pattern. The days of summer held bustling sports days and ballgames. In the wintertime, smoke rose in white plumes from a dozen homes marking their place in the valley. The clatter of harness and bells from horse-drawn cutters scattered their sound on the frosty air and socials and dances called the residents together more often. There was, I think, a sense of hope and confidence in the future.

It was towards the end of the next decade that change began, insidiously, slowly, as often is the pace of significant shifts. First, Ollie and Joy Anderson moved away from their farm on the northern ridge. Then, over a period of years, more farm homes became vacant. Each departure diminished the whole to some degree and the structure of the district slowly changed.

Often farmers from a distance came with big machines to tend the empty but fertile fields. "A natural evolution," my father said. But the outflow continued into the late 1960s when my parents, alone, remained in the valley. Like the many trees they had planted, their roots, too, were deep in the soil. In the end, though, they too moved away and left their farm to the wind, the rain, and the silent snow.

Sadly, all the components of a once active community are gone. The valley, though still tended and productive, lacks a human pulse. My parents are part of the statistics and the exodus which the magazine tells me is still ongoing. But, of course, the cold statistics do not tell of the dreams, the infused energy, the spent lives that fashioned, for such a short time, an unique social structure, a functioning and thriving community.

How does one account for the demise of such a community? The clues are contradictory and the answer eludes a non-pragmatic person such as I. Was it the lure of the city lights and distant places, an education (as it was for me), or a distaste for the simple rural life? Maybe it was the touted bad economics of farming. Nevertheless, the skeletons of the few homesteads which still cling to the fields and hillsides testify with certainty to a meaningful life style that is no more.

Perhaps, simply, my father was right: it was a natural evolution. But a sad change, I think. Our valley is still very green – and very empty.

16

The Mystery of Mister

Recent news from the scientific community tells us there is very little difference in the makeup of all species on earth, including humans. Genome mapping may explain why we have such an affinity with animals. Maybe that is why there was, for instance, such a special bond in the relationship Mom had with Mister during her last years on the farm.

A few years before Mom and Dad moved to town, a very special cat became part of their life. The animal came to their place from quite far away, they presumed, as there was no other inhabited place in the entire valley. It was a stray, and a sick one at that.

The cat found a hiding place among the straw bales on the south side of the garage. Mom caught only a glimpse of the animal, a large orange tomcat, emaciated, with wounds on his body. She placed a dish of milk and rice gruel at the entrance to his refuge and after a few days he did not run and hide when the dish was being filled.

The cat improved in health and trust. One morning when the June sun warmed the air and the bones of the old cat, he allowed Mom to pat his head and he purred loudly in response. He was likely to stick around, Mom thought, so he needed a name. Since he was a big cat with regal bearing, Fluffy or Kitty would not do. She decided on Mister and he soon responded to that name.

Mom and Mister became good friends. She talked to him during the long days she spent alone and when they walked together around the yard doing chores. He was a good listener and confidante and sometimes he would reply with a chorus of "meows" and always with deep, vibrating purring whenever she patted him.

Being a virile male of the species, his nature called him away occasionally for a short time, but he always returned, bedraggled and weary. So it was that he was away on one of his excursions when Mom and Dad made their planned move in mid-summer from the farm to the nearby town twenty miles away.

Mom was upset to leave without Mister and she searched and called for him, but in vain. When the moving trucks pulled out he was not with them.

The intent was to go back to the farm often to look for the cat and this Mom and Dad did but Mister was never there. They checked at the neighbours and in the nearby village but no one had seen a large orange brindle cat.

When I visited Mom and Dad in September that year, Mom and I drove out to the farm to look around the place and, in particular, to check again for Mister. We stood in the middle of the yard.

"Here Mister. Come here Mister," Mom called.

Then to our great joy, we heard a weak "meow" coming from under a nearby old wooden granary and the cat pushed himself out from under the building. It was Mister alright but in a sorry state. He was skin and bones, dirty, bruised, and his left back leg dragged.

He crawled towards Mom and she ran and gathered him into her arms. She sat on the back stairs of the house, opened a small container of milk and tried to have him lick some from her finger. He was too weak and too ill, although he "talked" to her with faint sounds as she caressed him with gentle strokes and words. They had indeed searched well for one another. Now she cradled him, rocking back and forth, aware that he was fading away. Suddenly he began purring loudly. He carried on for a minute or two, until his last heartbeat.

Mom took off her sweater, wrapped the sad little body in it and we buried Mister on the east side of the house, under the lilac bush. Thus, that silent farm site is not completely abandoned. It is home forever to the noble stray cat who brought companionship and unconditional love to Mom – and left a mystery for the family to ponder.

17

The Swale

I bought my grandson an acre of rain forest for his birthday. I am not sure this twenty-five dollar investment guarantees the survival of a piece of tropical rain forest, as advertised, but I like to think it does. Balancing the needs of the world's population with the need to sustain some ecological balance is an enormous and difficult problem I realize, but not an entirely new one. It was a concern once in our small corner of the world when I was a child.

At that time, our farm house sat at the top of a small rise in the treeless, windswept prairies. The land was drab and dusty during those drought years and, in an attempt to add some beauty to the place, Dad planted many young trees around the homestead, but most of those soon perished in the dry earth.

Thus, the green grass and trees that grew in a small swale two hundred metres across the road, in the neighbour's field, looked like paradise to us. The swale was a gentle depression in the flat land, a piece of original prairie the first owner, the pioneer, had left untouched, to be a green jewel in a sea of brown ploughed earth. A few saskatoon and willow bushes, together with a clump of gnarled poplar trees, one housing a robin's nest, grew there and its bottom was covered with woolly prairie grass and a few wild flowers. We called it "the Park." We children played there often, taking care not to harm any part of that precious space.

One day, after a trip to town, Dad had terrible news for us. The new owner of the land that the Park was on, a man fortunate to have a tractor then, intended to plough it under. It was, the man said, "in the way." We were distraught and fell to weeping and praying; but to no avail. The following Saturday morning, in early summer, the neighbour arrived at the swale on his tractor which had a scope-like apparatus attached to the front.

We stood in the lane that separated our land from his and watched in horror as the scope lowered, the tractor roared and moved into the Park. We shouted and screamed and stamped around as the machine, engulfed in noise and dust, ripped up the bushes, the trees, and the grass. I guess we, my two brothers and I, were staging an environmental protest. But it had no effect.

When the Park was totally gutted and we were spent with crying and yelling, we ran back into the house where Mother wiped our faces with a cold cloth. "There, there," she soothed, "maybe it will all grow back someday."

That was little comfort and we were not consoled. Someday, someday! We heard that refrain often. It was a philosophy, a notion, she and Dad and most drylanders clung to in order to survive: maybe it will rain someday soon, maybe the hopper cycle has passed.

And, in time, their faith was rewarded when the summer rains returned and produced abundant crops. But there was no resurrection for our Park. The willow bushes, the poplar trees, and the prairie grass did not grow back in the little swale. Our piece of virgin prairie was lost forever that summer day.

18

Lost in the Berry Patch

My daughter tells me she has picked a full pail of berries and plans to make some jam. She considers it a novel thing to do on a Sunday evening.

In my youth, berry picking was a necessary chore; sometimes it was fun and occasionally it even had an adventurous slant. My grandmother once got lost in the Sand Hills, while berry picking, and she not only created a panic in the community, but she also met an unexpected rescuer as she wandered around, trying to find her way out.

Although Grandmother was in her mid-seventies, she felt she had to do her share of berry picking. The preserves and jams made from saskatoon berries and chokecherries were much needed staples for the larders of early settlers, and Grandmother's pride demanded she should not be left behind when the family went out for the berry harvest.

In our part of the prairies, those berries grew most abundantly in a large uninhabited area, known locally as the Sand Hills, 15 miles south of our farm. It was a wild place, with bushes and trees and wet marshy areas. And it was there, on a hot July afternoon, that Grandmother strayed away from the rest of the family. Then, confused and frightened, she wandered further afield trying to find her way back. When a frantic search was made for her, she was not found before nightfall. The next morning, when reinforcements arrived, the search began again, accelerated by fears for the old lady alone in the rough and swampy land.

Meanwhile, Grandmother was battling her own fears. She had spent the night huddled under a stand of small trees, taking occasional sips from the water bottle she carried. At dawn, she started out again but after a while realized she was walking in circles. Thoroughly scared and very weary, Grandmother fell to her knees in despair, her face in her hands. When she looked up she was startled to see a dog nearby, sitting on its haunches and staring at her. It was a mid-size, black and white mongrel.

She rose slowly, fearful of the animal, and began walking away from it, in the direction she hoped would take her out of the woods. The dog jumped up and ran in front of her, turned and, baring his teeth, snarled at her. She felt a sense of panic and went quickly in another direction. Again the dog barred her way. This was repeated again, increasing Grandmother's fears.

The dog ran to the opposite side, stopped and looked back at her over his shoulder. "It seems," she thought, "he wants me to follow him, but in the wrong direction!" Still, she was a prisoner of the animal and so she walked behind him, hoping he would soon run off. The dog led the way, running ahead but always waiting for her to catch up. Branches scratched her arms and face and snagged her clothes as she pushed her way through thick bushes, and her shoes filled with mud in the swampy areas. She was exhausted and confused, but she trudged along, sure they were heading further into the tangled depths of the Sand Hills.

So Grandmother was amazed when after an hour or two, the dog led her out of the bushes into a clearing. She recognized the open countryside in front of her; home was ten miles away down a nearby trail. She sat down and happily shared the remaining water with the dog. "You are my friend, my pal," she said and he allowed her to pat him.

As she started down the trail towards home, the dog held back at the edge of the bush.

"Come on," Grandmother called, "Come on Pal," and the dog followed her.

This time she led the way. There were no farms in sight, where she might have gone for help, so they walked along, stopping every mile or two to rest at the side of the trail or in the shade of one of the few trees that grew by the wayside. When she did so, the dog sat beside her, waiting patiently to resume the journey. The day was hot and Grandmother was exhausted, hungry, and thirsty. Her pace slowed and the dog adjusted his gait, walking close beside her.

Finally, they trudged up the last hill to home, together, side by side, in the warm evening. Mother was the first to see them as they came around the barn. She ran to Grandmother, while calling out the good news to the searchers who had come in for an evening meal. Laughing and crying, chiding her and hugging her, the family and friends gathered around, while off to one side Pal sat and watched.

Grandmother was too weary to say much – only a request that Auntie feed the new dog – before she fell into bed. But, in the morning, what a story she had to tell!

Pal enjoyed the extra attention he received from Grandmother, but he never seemed to really belong to us. And one day, a year later, he just disappeared. We searched the countryside and inquired at all the neighbors but there was no trace of him. He was gone, as mysteriously as he had arrived.

19

The Light in the Curve of the Road

Over the years I have garnered enough information from family and friends, and from my own experience to be convinced that we do occasionally encounter situations where fact, logic and perception do not coordinate. Though unexplained mysteries may add flavour to life, sometimes they can be quite unsettling.

One such event occurred some decades ago. At that time our family lived on a farm fifteen miles from the town where our grandparents lived. One day in late August, we visited them, and after supper and a game of ball we climbed into Dad's old truck and headed home in the dark of a warm, windy night.

When we left town Dad took the "cut-off," a dirt trail that ran across country and shortened the journey home by three or four miles. It ran along beside the railroad track and was hemmed in by trees and bushes on the other side.

The railroad track bed elevated gradually, and we had to cross that track. Two miles out of town, the dirt trail made a sharp turn to the left and then crossed the track by going up the steep grade, over the tracks and down again on the other side.

My two brothers and I sat in the back, in the truck box, on the seat Dad had saved when he converted his old Model A Ford car. We leaned back against the cab wherein Mom and Dad sat, one child between them and the baby on Mom's knee. The night was dark, even starless, as heavy clouds driven by a strong wind pulsed across the sky. The wind rattled the tin engine hood and yanked at the side curtains as the truck laboured – well loaded as it was – into the face of the wind.

As I was standing up in the back, holding on to the top edge of the cab, I saw the piece of lumber as soon as Dad did. We were close to the turn in the dirt trail when the headlights of the truck reflected off a board laying at the edge of the trail, at the base of a grove of dark trees. It gleamed brightly, demanding attention. It appeared to be three or four feet long. It had, perhaps, dropped from some passing vehicle. I thought Dad would pick it up and check with our neighbors. Such a fine piece of lumber would come in handy to mend the barn door or build a shelf.

Dad slowed the truck, stopping in the curve just below the steep crossing. He stepped out of the truck and froze, suddenly engulfed in a bright light. From around a slight bend in the tracks, the brilliant headlight of a train suddenly pierced the darkness. Immediately the air was filled with sound and fury. A huge locomotive thundered by, spewing fire and smoke, shaking the earth. It was unaware of the flimsy truck and the small persons there below it in the dark.

Dad stood motionless, staring at the train as the rail cars banged and clattered past. I jumped down and went to stand beside him. Finally the caboose went by and there was relative stillness except for the wind blowing through the trees.

"Let's go Dad," I said.

As if with afterthought, Dad looked towards the spot where we had seen the lumber, the piece we had stopped to pick up. We could not see it, not even in the light from the truck headlights. We searched carefully for that piece of white wood, walking up and down, parting the grass and looking under the bushes. Dad got down on his hands and knees and fiercely searched the area. He found only short sticks, dirty and grey, part of a tree branch, and he put them back exactly where they had lain, there in the curve of the road.

We did not talk about this incident, not until years later, and then only briefly and without comment.

20

A Profound Revelation
on an August Evening

"Myths which are believed in tend to become true." This quotation from George Orwell has proven its veracity many times it seems to me, and was once again confirmed on a recent summer evening. My neighbor Betty and I were sitting in my backyard enjoying a warm late August evening and making idle chatter. She stood up to go home.

"Days have begun to shorten noticeably," she said. "Look, it is only 9 o'clock and darkness is already falling."

I winced at that reference to darkness since I have strong feelings on the subject. Why do people still use those old misleading clichés: "dusk falls," "night falls?" Even Longfellow had the audacity to say: "Darkness falls from the wings of night, as a feather is wafted downward." It is difficult to change false beliefs, Lord knows, and this misinformation – that darkness descends or "falls" – is still being foisted on a gullible populace by pen and poet.

I know better. My brother and I resolved this controversy many years ago, when we were 11 and 12 years old at the age of total enlightenment. We made a particularly astute observation of the shift from day to night. The opportunity to do so presented itself one warm August evening, much like the one Betty and I were sharing.

We left the high, hilly land where Dad pastured the cattle, going down a dirt road between fields of ripened grain, to our home in the valley. Lady, the big farm horse pulling the buggy we rode in, steadfastly maintained her usual slow walking pace, although to do so she had to lean back into the buggy shafts to offset the gravitational force, which otherwise may have urged her into a trot. That slow descent gave us plenty of time to watch the transformation of the countryside from day to night.

"It looks pretty dark at home," Larry said. We noticed from our vantage point that the valley below was already softened with a grey dusk. The coulees and ravines at the side of our road were filled with cool shadows and the bushes around the slough were silhouetted black against the water, which still reflected a bright sky.

The hills on the north, the opposite rim of the valley, were flushed by the lingering rays of the sunset. A car, coming down the road, its headlights directing its descent, left behind a trail of rose-colored dust.

We watched the twilight on the land intensify and fingers of black move out from between the hills and from the coulees and spread across the fields. Lights at farm homes came on, landmarks merged and disappeared in the gathering gloaming and yet, we noted, the sky above was streaked with light and shifting colours of rose and orange. The brightness overhead began to fade and the darkness which had enveloped the land flowed up and across the sky, pushing back the remaining fragments of sunset. The last bit of light clung tenaciously to the horizon. We watched it slip away and the canopy of the night sky settle along the western hills.

As we drove into the farmyard, in the warm, dark night, our musing and discussion ceased. We had come to the simple conclusion that darkness does not fall; rather it starts on the ground and pushes its way across the land, then up into the sky and all the way to the western horizon.

But I won't bother trying to explain that fact again to another contrary or cynical person. My neighbour Betty will never know the truth.

Autumn

21

Osprey

In our part of the world, the ebb and flow of distinct seasons propels massive changes in our environment. This triggers one of the phenomena in which I am most interested since I am a bird-watcher – the migration of the birds each spring and autumn.

While our summertime birds leave for Mexico or the southern USA in the fall, others from the far north fly into our area, considering this south enough for them. When I was growing up on a prairie farm, snowbirds were a common sight in the wintertime. Those white birds, officially known as snow buntings, nest in the Arctic regions and come south to our prairies in late autumn. They often swooped and swirled into our farmyard in tight formation, settled upon stark trees, chirping in merry consultation, then flew off again, disappearing into the falling snow which always seemed to accompany them.

Again this fall, with a sense of wonderment, and a bit of melancholy, I watched the ragged V formation of honking geese fly overhead and the flocks of ducks and small birds depart. By August's end, the sea gulls had gathered in their staging zone, in the park across the road, and then one day they were gone, flying in a north-westerly direction, presumably taking the long way south.

My special friends, the small osprey clan, have gone south. I checked on their riverside nest a few weeks ago, on a warm sunny October afternoon when the last leaves were drifting down from the trees. The nest sits atop a telephone pole in the middle of a swampy area, a basket-like structure about two feet square in full relief against the blue sky. It looked sad and deserted that day, like an empty old house, void of the intense activity that had been evident there throughout the summer. Despite its seemingly precarious perch, a source of concern for me all year, it had proved to be sufficiently stable to house the rambunctious offspring who grew up there this year.

The osprey belongs to the hawk family; it is dark brown with white underside, about 24 inches long from beak to tail and the wing span can be up to five feet. My grandsons, Michael and Alexander, and I became acquainted with the osprey family in the spring. Our interest was piqued when we learned that the survival of the species has been threatened, mainly by the pesticides contaminating the fish they eat.

When we first discovered the nest, the mother was already incubating her eggs, hunkered down and indifferent to our prying eyes. We stood on the river path, about one hundred yards away, and used Michael's binoculars, which he got with three cereal box tops and two dollars. We had a fair view of the nest and its occupants.

On our next visit, two or three weeks later, the nest was full of squawking birds and we could see a few bobbing heads and open mouths. Mother or Father osprey made constant forays to the river for food. The birds grew quickly and soon we counted the gaping mouths reaching up on long skinny necks, and decided there were three youngsters.

A month or two later the nest was overflowing with the gangling fledglings – complaining, demanding, bickering. They were almost as big as their parents.

"Which one is the mother?" Alex asked.

"The tired-looking one," I said.

In July we had a violent summer storm. The strong winds blew branches off my backyard poplar tree and sent garbage cans rolling down the alley. As I watched the wind bending the trees, I wondered what was happening to the osprey nest atop its pole. After the storm abated I went to see. Happily I found the nest, a conglomeration of sticks woven by an unschooled bird, intact and still housing its full complement of young birds.

On our last visit to the family, the smell and feel of autumn was in the air. We found the nest empty except for one of the grown offspring. It seemed to be trying to muster courage to fly. It stood on one edge of the nest stretching and flapping its wings and then hopped to the other side to do the same thing. We watched with amusement for a while, equating its antics with that of a human adolescent. The shrill whistle from an unseen parent assured us it was still nearby.

If all goes well with the osprey family in their southern home, they'll be back when the seasons change again. We will be waiting for them.

22

Homeless

The current level of poverty and homelessness in our country is not a new phenomenon, as we who remember the Dirty Thirties can attest. However, this time around, I am for the most part removed from the reality of the situation, and my attitude has been one of indifference. That outlook changed after a recent trip to Toronto.

I found the city vibrant and exciting. Joanne, my daughter, and I spent one afternoon browsing through one of the largest malls, marvelling at the massive array of opulent and ordinary merchandise for sale. We were hurrying home, down a side street, our heads lowered into the wind and the rain of the cold autumn day, when I stumbled over a bundle of blankets piled against a doorway.

I stopped abruptly. The bundle of clothes and ragged blankets encompassed a face, pinched and young, and as grey as the blanket draped over the head and shoulders. Nothing was said as we stared at one another. I fumbled in my purse, for some money I guess, but Joanne urged me on, reminding me that the area was not safe.

I had a flash of déja vu: another time, another place. Years ago I had seen such a face. It belonged to a young man who was homeless and hungry.

He had come, during the Great Depression, to my grandparents' house in a small prairie town, begging for something to eat. The land was awash with men drifting across the country in search of work and he, among others, had stopped in our town.

I was standing behind Grandmother's skirt when she opened the door to the man's knock. I stared at him and at his tattered clothes and mismatched shoes before I was shooed into the "safety" of the kitchen.

I ran to a side window and peered out between the geranium pots. He stood silently at the back door waiting for a handout, a young man with dark curly hair; he looked like my Uncle Ted who was in Grade 12 that year.

Grandmother gave him a sandwich and a glass of milk. Although my grandparents were poor, there was always enough to eat at their house, due in large part to their frugal nature and to the big garden and the small flock of chickens raised in a corner of the yard.

Later that evening Grandfather delivered a box to the railroad station. He was sending back a clock he had repaired. I went with him, trotting along behind.

The station was on the outskirts of the village and as we neared it we heard the sound of a mouth organ. Someone was playing *Danny Boy* while others whistled along.

"Those guys," Grandfather informed me, "are hobos, and best you should stay away." They camped unseen from general view in a willow grove on the other side of the tracks. Mostly young men, like the one I had seen begging for food, they travelled from town to town riding clustered together on the top of freight trains. Hobos travelled light, but it was easy to pack along a mouth organ.

We left the box at the station and headed home. The mellow evening light, peculiar to the prairies, softened the parched landscape and cast long shadows behind each familiar building. As Grandfather strode down the dusty lane carrying me piggy-back, the melancholy music trailed along behind us until we reached home.

That year the war clouds were gathering in Europe and when conflict broke out the following year, many of those unemployed young men joined the armed forces. Ironically, then, for the purpose of war, there was food for them, and a bed. And dignity.

It does seem, even in this highly technical and sophisticated world, that some things do not change. I wonder what will become of that young person, that child of our land, whom I stumbled over on that cold, windy, Toronto street.

Moneca and young brother in Granddad's garden

23

A Stroll Through the Past

Recently, Sunnybrook Farm Museum, an Agricultural Interpretive Centre in Red Deer, had a two-day celebration, and everyone was invited. I attended and I took Matthew and Jessica with me, to show them some of the items their pioneer great-great-grandparents used.

The day began with a pancake breakfast. Then we browsed through an interesting and extensive display of farm machinery, some dating back to the turn of the last century, and we reminisced about items common and essential to the farming operation of yesteryear. There were sheds full of artifacts: butter churns, separators, kerosene lamps, medical equipment, and wash boards, to name but a few.

We looked at the long row of ploughs. They ranged from the small hand-guided plough, pulled by two horses, to the larger units. The wheeled sulky, or gang plough, turned two furrows using four to six horses, and the four-bottom plough required ten to twelve horses to pull it. These units had a seat of molded steel for the driver, which we now sometimes find at garage sales. Besides guiding his horses – the wise animals knew their business well and needed little directing – the driver adjusted the depth of the furrow with a lever at his side.

"Where are the big ploughs?" I asked my friend Ted. "Bigger than this?" he asked with a puzzled look.

I felt obliged then to tell him about the twelve-bottom plough, (the mother of all ploughs) my grandparents had long ago. Because of its size, it needed more than horsepower to do its job. It was pulled by the steam engine Granddad had, which was a large, fearsome looking vehicle, and required a raging fire in its belly in order to move. Then it was carefully attended to by a "fireman" as well as the driver.

No doubt it was an awesome sight. That strange looking machine lumbered across the landscape pulling behind it a plough that turned twelve furrows at once, transforming miles of grassland into warm brown earth in a day. The round, even furrows turned up to the warm sun enticed Grandmother to shed her shoes and walk barefoot across the aromatic earth when she took lunch to the crew. Seagulls followed the plodding machine, hovering over the dark soil left in its wake. It moved, at right angles to the road, across the flats and over the gentle hills, creating a new look for the prairies.

When the plough was being pulled, three or four men stood on its broad plank platform to operate the levers which, at the end of each row, were used to raise (and then lower again) all twelve shares so that the plough could be turned around. It was cumbersome in this respect, but otherwise was an admirable piece of machinery, solidly built and designed to fulfill a special purpose at that time in history. It turned many quarters of virgin land for my Granddad and also for many other settlers in the area.

But by about 1915, the steam engine and, with it, the huge ploughs fell into disuse. According to Lyle, who works at the Interpretive Center, the big steam engines, moving at two to three miles per hour, were too slow for other uses. Many years after its heyday, Granddad's steam engine, rusted and humbled, was hauled away and sold for scrap.

A less drastic fate befell the mighty twelve-bottom plough. It was left to deteriorate amongst the trees at the bottom of the yard. My brother and I often played on its broken wooden platform, grass and bushes pushing up through cracked boards. The steel frame, minus ploughshares, seemed to sink slowly, year by year, into the soft ground. Perhaps in time it will turn into a fossil, a sort of dinosaur of ploughs.

There were many tractors at the exhibit and I searched in vain for an Emerson, like the one Dad once had. The Emerson was unusual amongst tractors, having one large full-width steel wheel in the front and two regular ones in the back. As long as I can remember, it sat where it had been driven, or dragged, to a spot under the trees in the windbreak, its past glory and usefulness, like that of the steam engine and the plough, obscured in antiquity. One day, Dad sold it to a travelling connoisseur of tractors for seventy-five dollars and, I understand, it now sits, restored and elegant, in some museum.

An afternoon viewing the exhibit at the Museum made for a nostalgic stroll through the past. I recognized most of the implements and the gadgets, and recited to Matthew, Jessica, and their Dad, and anyone else within hearing range, the ways our ancestors used them. The settlers were a resourceful bunch, making many of the things they needed, such as cord and ropes made with the rope-weaving machine I spotted in a corner.

The museum is a wonderful tribute to our heritage. I hope that young people – including my grandchildren, share my appreciation for those artifacts and the folks who used them years ago.

The "Grande Dame" of the threshing operation

24

High Society

Children today participate in many extra-curricular activities. I am amazed at the dizzying pace my grandkids keep. Lillian, my next-door neighbour, tells me that her granddaughter, already involved in sports, drama and music, has begun dancing lessons so that she can attend a "coming out" party.

The children who grew up on the prairies during the Depression and war years had quite a different avenue to a similar goal. It was like everything then – a do-it-yourself project. In this way, the year I turned 14 was made most memorable. One event stands out. In the fall I was introduced, or rather pushed, into the social life of our farming community.

It wasn't my idea. My parents decided it was time for me to take part in local events and dances instead of spending all my free time reading or riding around the countryside on old Queenie. As if to facilitate their plans, a dance had been scheduled for our local schoolhouse one Friday evening at the end of September. By then the harvest was done, the gardens dug up, and the autumn days were still warm and mellow. Dad made plans for us to attend.

This would be my second attempt at integrating into the local social scene, meagre as it was. The first try was a complete disaster. In the spring of the same year, before Lent, Dad had taken me to a dance in the same building. That was where I went to school, and at once I headed for the familiar cloakroom. I spent the entire evening there among the coats. When John, a neighbour, had tried to pry me loose for a dance, I fiercely clung to the coat hangers. Dad's attempt, made with gentle persuasion, had no better results. On the way home, I sensed his displeasure.

I had been to many of these gatherings when I was younger as Mom and Dad took all five of us children along whenever they attended. But then I could be anonymous, a part of the group of children who sat together at the back or slept on the coats piled on the desks pushed back against the walls. Those outings stopped when the new baby sister arrived. Packing up five kids and a baby was just too much for Mom.

This time, Dad was determined there would be no such shenanigans as there were in the spring. Mom, who would accompany us, agreed with him. Sensing their determination, I was resigned to my fate. I put on the purple velvet dress Mom had made out of one Aunt Carol had discarded. A pair of slightly mended silk stockings with seams up the back, that would not stay straight on my skinny legs, completed the ensemble. Mom put a dab of her Evening in Paris cologne behind each of my ears. I felt quite lovely.

Mom and Dad sat in the buggy seat guiding the horse along the well-travelled road. Real horse-power provided the means of transportation then. Dad's old Ford sat in the garage for many years for want of repairs impossible to obtain during the war years. Furthermore, gasoline was rationed and there seemed to be very little even for the old Case tractor. Perhaps it needed repairs as well.

Despite the purpose of the trip, I was elated to be going out with Mom and Dad, to spend some special time with them alone. I stood tall on the back platform of the buggy holding on to the front seat, my head in the starlit sky, the breeze whipping my hair and my skirt around as we drove along, past all the familiar landmarks I knew and loved – the bush with the saskatoon berries, the grove of aspen trees, and the small coulee where the coyotes had their den.

The schoolhouse was filled with people, chatter and the white light from the hanging gas lamp. I went immediately to the cloakroom. When the music started, Dad looked into the room, but I asked him to wait for a slow dance. All too soon, the musicians, a fiddler and an accordionist, started *The Tennessee Waltz* and I grimly emerged from my sanctuary. Dad and I began to dance.

My knees were locked and I plodded along stiff-legged, certain everyone was looking at me. "One, two, three," Dad whispered as he firmly guided me around the small floor. I noticed no one, except Mom, was watching us and other couples gliding by were indifferent. Dad was a good dancer and I managed to follow him.

One, two, three. Suddenly my knees unlocked and I was moving to the music. I relaxed and sensed the rhythm. And then we swayed and dipped as we swirled around the floor. My heart was beating rapidly and my head was swimming with exhilaration.

"That was okay," I said to Dad as we walked back to the cloak room. We had one other dance and John, the neighbour, asked me for one too. Paul showed me how to do the polka, and we whirled around and around.

We drove home at a good clip as Queenie was wont to do when homeward bound. I stood tall in the back part of the buggy, my head again brushing the starlit sky, but I was in a different space, filled with the magic of the evening – a magic that was forever unmatched, even when I danced years later at the Royal York in Toronto and at other grand places. Mom and Dad chatted about the evening, but my mind was full of music and joy and new realities. I had been successfully "launched" in the manner and style that was common then – much different from today, but just as wonderful.

25

Touched by a Prairie Flower Child

Sharing a room in a hospital creates instant bonding and a closeness that would take some time to develop elsewhere. Perhaps it is the impersonal atmosphere prevalent in the large building that draws room-mates together. In any event, Anna and I became friends and confidantes during the three days I was there.

She reminded me of my mother, or perhaps my grandmother – spry, slim and straight, in her early 90s, with a head of silver hair fashionably styled. Her faded beauty made me think, as other such persons have, of a flower garden in autumn, a melancholy garden, with sparse and wispy blossoms and tangled foliage. But once, we know, that garden was colourful and vibrant.

Anna liked to talk about the past and I was eager to hear her stories.

"We had little education," she said. She touched on the subject of education a number of times. "We lived four miles from school and when Dad needed the horses, or when there wasn't enough feed for them, we walked to school, even in the winter time. We got up at five o'clock, and we could not go back to bed like I can now. We had to feed the horses and do the milking before we went to school."

"I married very young. My sister-in-law told me Pete was no good – he was a liar. She was right; but I married him anyway. I had to work in logging camps as a cook and I hiked around the country by myself. I spent many years in the bush where it was quiet and clean and the new green smelled so good in the spring."

Anna told me she had two children, a girl and a boy. Her son died when he was a teenager and she felt like crawling into the grave with him. "Part of me died then," she said.

"My daughter keeps telling me to write my memoirs even though there is nothing much to say. But my grandson, who went to university, writes wonderful prose and poetry and can paraphrase a story like the very dickens!" she added with pride.

On my last evening in the hospital, when the door had been closed to the noise in the hallway for the night and the setting sun filled the room with soft light, gentle and reflective conversation came easily.

Anna reminisced about the hard life her parents had, and the joyful times too. She told me about the little house she bought in a small town "for a decent price," after she retired, and, by herself, built new cupboards and planted trees and a lilac bush. Her mother had always loved lilacs but they grew poorly on the homestead. "Now," she said, "I will move again, for the last time, into a nursing home."

After a short silence, Anna spoke wistfully into the darkening room. "Where did the past 50 years go? Where did life go? When we were young, we thought it would never end. We can't run up to it and touch it and say 'here we are; wait for us.'"

I could not respond, moved by this bit of poetry from an old, prairie flower child. But then, I should not have been surprised: I had already decided she was the prototype of pioneer women, those strong, nurturing women who were wonderfully shaped by great hardships and who touched the lives of many people, even as Anna touched mine. She inadvertently reminded me that most of us can claim an ancestor or two in that category. And I am grateful for that too.

26

The Importance of Being October

October is a month of reckoning for man and nature. The growing season is finished; the land is hunkering down awaiting winter. An important and pivotal role in the turning of the seasons belongs to October.

On the prairies, October spends its allotted days moving our landscape from a warm autumn on the edge of summer with leafy trees and growing grass to quite a different scene by month's end. Then the fields lie empty and the trees – like the ones in my backyard – stand resigned and bare, and the brown pasture may be dusted with snow.

When I lived on the farm with my parents, harvest was an exciting and exhilarating time. It was usually finished by the first of October. I am a city dweller now, but I still need to touch base with the land at this time of the year. Thus, in mid-September, we drove into the country to enjoy the splendour of a prairie autumn. The day was warm and windless, as harvest days should be, and dust and grain chaff hung in the amber air. We heard the hum of a distant combine; it was creeping across a field, like some big beetle, gathering the faded straw.

There are many activities crammed into October's thirty-one days, including Thanksgiving Day. On the farm, many years ago, we celebrated Thanksgiving in grand style, with the gathering together of our big family to celebrate, give thanks and feast upon the bounty produced by a year's labour. Not only were all the vegetables grown on the farm, but the turkey was home-grown too.

Each spring, Mother picked one tom from her small brood of young turkeys to be "groomed" for the Thanksgiving dinner in the fall. One year, that bird, being well-fed, grew so large and so bossy he was a menace, not only to other barnyard fowl, but to the small children in the family. At the least excuse he would strut about in full regalia, tail feathers fanned, wing tips to the ground, and his wattles flaming red as he loudly proclaimed his imperial position.

But pride goeth before the fall: one September day, in some covert operation, the chosen one was dispatched, "dressed" and placed in the deep freeze. Memory of the bird faded. Then on Thanksgiving Day, roasted golden brown and stuffed with Mother's special dressing, the turkey graced our table.

And it was a big table, seating our family of eight, the grandparents, an aunt or two and a couple of local bachelors. Grateful for the invitation, the bachelors always arrived early, "looking rather spiffy" Mother said, with a bottle of chokecherry wine for her and an admiring eye for the aunts. Sometimes the overflow, generally the youngest children, was seated at an improvised table – made with boxes and boards and a clean white sheet – in the living room, from where they clamoured loudly for "more turkey, more pumpkin pie!" Thanksgiving Day has been celebrated, more or less, in the same manner over the years.

October's temperature hustles the animals into hibernation, chases the birds south and compels everyone to prepare fields, yards and homes for a new reality. By the end of the month, nature has settled down for the coming winter and we have been persuaded to put aside any longing for warm and balmy days. For such weather we must wait for the arrival of spring.

27

A Hallowe'en Tale

In October, the daylight hours dwindle as do the remaining days of the year. There isn't much to celebrate now. That is why we make the most of Hallowe'en at the end of the month. The children, especially, relish that day for the fun in dressing up in outlandish costumes and having parental permission to demand candy from strangers, and for the possibility of an encounter or two with some scary mystery.

One year, my brother Larry and I had a Hallowe'en we have never forgotten. That year Mom took us to the nearest town, fifteen miles away, where our grandparents lived, so that we could experience the "dress-up, trick or treat" aspect of Hallowe'en.

We left our farm in late afternoon, travelling by horse and buggy. Larry and I, aged nine and eleven, urged speed, but Mom moved us along at a rate she thought comfortable for the horse which, nevertheless, brought us to town in good time. Larry was dressed as a hobo, a costume not difficult to fashion in those post-depression days, and I considered myself a gypsy, garbed in Mom's old dress, beads and bangles, and my face dabbed with rouge and lipstick. We were each equipped with a medium-sized sugar sack in anticipation of a successful evening.

At dusk, we left Grandmother's place and went up and down the streets to each house, with cries of "Trick or Treat," tentatively at first, though the pronouncements grew louder and bolder as the evening went on. The town was small – 500 souls. The streets that night were full of children running around, unchaperoned, in search of goodies and fun.

By the time the cover of darkness, punctured by a few street lights, settled upon the town, Larry and I had reached the outskirts where the houses eased into the bushy and treed landscape. We hollered our demands at each door on that last street, right down to the end house.

It was an unpainted one-and-a-half story structure set back from the road, with much of the yard reclaimed by encroaching bushes. In the faint light from a distant street lamp, we eagerly ran up the weed-strewn cinder pathway to the tilting porch.

"Trick or treat!" we yelled. "Hall-o-we'en apples, hallo-o-we'en apples," we sang.

Quite suddenly, an old, gray-haired lady stood in the doorway smiling down at us. Her hair was gathered in a loose knot on the top of her head and she wore a long, black dress with a shawl over her stooped shoulders.

The room behind her was lit with soft dim light from a kerosene lamp. I saw a rocking chair with a red and green afghan thrown across the back. Without speaking, the lady put a popcorn ball into each of our proffered sugar sacks.

A cat came from the room and rubbed against the lady's skirt. I had never seen such a strange coloured cat before – it was spotted in orange and black, brown and white. The lady reached to the side and then put a handful of Hallowe'en candy kisses into Larry's sack and another handful into mine. She was more generous than anyone else had been. We thanked her and ran off with our loot.

Back at Grandmother's house, Mom examined the contents of our sacks and asked where we got the popcorn balls. They were an unusual treat. I told her from the house next to the Jensens.

"Do you mean the old story-and-a-half place with the cinder sidewalk?" Grandmother asked. I nodded.

"Can't be," she said, "you kids must be dreaming. Old Mrs. Delly lived there and she died five years ago. The place has been vacant ever since."

"She was a strange one," Grandmother went on. "She had nothing to do with anybody. Had no family, just that stupid calico cat. They died the same day you know."

"Imagine," she sniffed, "being buried with a cat!"

Larry and I stared at one another. We were confused and frightened. The joy which our Hallowe'en haul had generated quickly diminished, and was completely squelched when Mom threw out the popcorn balls.

We drove home that night under the light of a half moon which shone fitfully between drifting clouds. We did not dare glance back at the dark dust swirling behind the buggy wheels. We sat mute and wide-eyed and as close to Mom as possible.

28

Tom and Lucy

When we drive through the countryside today we still see a few deserted farmhouses, sad and silent relics of the past. They stand in the midst of wheat fields, weather-beaten and hollow-eyed. Once they were home to pioneer families. One of them housed my friends Tom and Lucy.

After the First World War, Tom and Lucy emigrated from England. Transplanted city dwellers, they had come to farm on the great plains, and that they did with much vigour and hard work. Decades later they sold the farm and moved into town, buying the small brown bungalow next to my grandparents. It was then I got to know them.

They had hoped to visit the old country but, for various reasons, that dream had not been fulfilled and it faded as time went by. Tom started a small business, the town's first nursery, located on a piece of sandy land down by the railroad tracks. Small willows already grew there and he uprooted some of them to plant young lilac bushes, maples, and spruce seedlings. Each spring he grew flats of yellow marigolds and purple petunias.

Tom derived much joy and pleasure – though little profit – from that venture. He gave away many of the bushes. I was the recipient of some small lilac shoots that grew to enhance our farmyard. Tom always had time to talk to the children (he had none of his own) as he tended the plants in his slow methodical way, coaxing them – the plants and the children – to grow and bloom.

Lucy, though, had a different nature. The fact that she and her husband were poor had not dampened her self-esteem. She took an appropriate job, that of town librarian, and became active in community and church affairs, teaching our Sunday School class with firm opinion and steely authority.

Often in the summertime, Tom would walk down the dusty streets, in the amber-shaded evening, to the railroad station to watch a train thunder in. The noise, the smell, the steam, and the unknown faces at the coach windows brought an intriguing sense of distant places to our little town. There would be a quick exchange of passengers and freight and then the train pulled out. Tom longed to board one someday for a trip, maybe to England in the springtime. Until then, he would watch the trains and listen to their shrill, mournful whistle as they pulled in and out of town.

One evening in mid-November as Tom and Lucy sat reading in their living room, as was their custom, a train was going through town. Its unusually loud whistle filled their room, rattling the dishes in the sideboard and startling Lucy. She looked up. Tom's head had slumped forward and his book had fallen to the floor. Lucy said later it seemed as if the train had called to him and at last he could go.

Tom was buried in the hillside cemetery beside the other old timers. Lucy sold the bungalow and went back to England, and after a few years no one heard from her any more. Except for a few lilac bushes, there is no tangible evidence of their sojourn in our community.

29

November's Face

Yesterday was a dreary and cold November day, with leaden skies and a nippy northwest breeze. That snapped me out of my lethargic comfort zone, induced by the long warm autumn and the golden Indian Summer days we have enjoyed. The arrival of November urges us to make last minute preparations for the coming new reality, the winter season.

I have little to do outside since I now live in an apartment. Mainly, I watch the seasonal transitions occur in the park across the street. I did put the deck chairs away, but I could not bring myself to uproot and throw out the only pot of petunias growing on my deck. Since my deck is now my only garden space, I have an exaggerated attachment to the plants. It was late spring when I finally got around to buying them – a flat of scraggy petunias found under the counter at the nursery and destined for the garbage.

The plants rewarded me all summer long, flourishing in the fresh soil in the big wooden tub – a wealth of colour, purple and red and pink, scenting the evening air and each morning flirting with the bees.

Now it is autumn and they are again scraggy with twisted stems and small blossoms reaching for the pale sun. I will leave the tub and its plants there, on the other side of the patio door, to be my "companion" all winter long.

My hands-on involvement with jobs that were special to the different seasons was not so minimal, or whimsical, years ago. The autumn months then were filled with monumental tasks centred around the harvest and preparations for the winter.

Starting in October, or even earlier, potatoes and vegetables were dug up and carried into our earth-floored cellar, dozens of jars of fruit and jams were stored in colorful rows, the hay was stacked behind the barn and the cattle brought home from the community pasture. But the most important and timely job was the grain harvest: cutting, stooking and threshing.

In those pre-combine days, everyone looked forward to the arrival of the threshers. When the threshing outfit trekked up our hill, it looked like a circus parade to the excited children. First came a battered truck, then a droning tractor, an old Case, pulling the "grande dame" of the procession, the mighty threshing machine. It was followed by six hayracks pulled by sturdy horses of different colours.

We children were told to stay out of the way, but we hung around the periphery of the feverish activity, absorbing the smells, the sounds and the excitement.

After the threshers moved on, all work seemed anti-climactic. But we finished with the garden, hung some marigolds and asters to dry for winter bouquets, confined the laying hens to their roomy coop, and Dad filled the coal bin to the top. The land was without colour. Under low grey skies, the short days were dreary and cool. That was the face of November and it drove us indoors where life was easier and more restful, and we were glad for that.

It is that time of the year again and the same dramatic shift is apparent, even in this urban landscape, though now my intimate contact with nature is limited to my relationship with the tub of petunias. Maybe next year I will expand the garden on my deck.

Winter

30

Winter Weather Drama

No doubt the prairie winter of 1995-1996 has found its way into the record books. Not only were the temperatures extremely cold for weeks on end, but the snowfall was unusually heavy. By mid-November a generous blanket covered the land. I watched the snow fall, heavy and silent, on our town, on our street, curtaining off the park across the road and muting all noise so that the cars glided soundlessly in and out of view along the adjoining avenue. I battled the white stuff, shovelling it in ever-higher mounds along the sidewalks and I felt claustrophobic when it drifted in piles against my door.

Yet that is a far cry from the fears provoked by other winters.

"We have to go back to the 1930s," the television weatherman had said, "to find a winter equivalent to this one for cold temperatures and snowfall." He may be right, but I for one, take no comfort in such a reminder! I need little prompting to recall a couple of winters from that era that were extremely severe and harsh – especially from the viewpoint of a young child.

Then, it seemed, snow-laden clouds hovered over the land most of the time. Deep snow covered the fences with wind-hardened drifts and we drove to school straight across country, disregarding signs and property lines. Often the howling winds swirled the snow in roof-high drifts around the house. One year, an enormous bank of snow firmly blocked our view from the kitchen window and treated us daily to shifting blue shadows on its concave side, and sometimes to a rose flush at sunset.

When the temperature dropped dangerously low one January day, Dad drove by horse and sleigh to his mother's place. She and a daughter lived alone on the original homestead one-and-a-half miles away. Our thermometer slid to a record minus 53 degrees Fahrenheit and we became anxious as we waited for his return. The afternoon visit of an hour or two that he had intended stretched to dusk, and then to nightfall, and still he was not back. Mother tried to hide her fears as she lit the kerosene lamp and prepared a meal for the young children. If Dad were really in trouble, what could she do to help him?

Mother sent my older brother Larry, who was eleven years old, and me outside to see what we could to the east, across the fields to Grandmother's house. We stepped out into a strange world. The air was still, sharp and frozen; it cut my lungs and jabbed at my face even through a heavy scarf. The stars spread thick and they were brilliant and low, hanging in the upper branches of the big poplar tree. In the starlight, the white land shimmered and glowed and the very air seemed to flicker – as if sprinkled with fairy dust. The snow under our boots creaked and we felt inclined to whisper to one another.

The scene was eerie and captivating and we might have stood there, beside the house forever, but for Dad's voice. Sound carries well in clear cold air, a phenomenon Larry and I already knew. Yet we were startled when we heard Dad yell instructions to Grandmother: "Now take care and watch the stove." There was a murmured reply and then we heard the jingle of harness as he started the team for home. Mother rapped nervously on the window for us to come in, but we were reluctant to move. Then she rapped again.

As Larry and I warmed ourselves by the stove, Mom, watching through the window, saw Dad put the horses into the barn. When he walked into the kitchen I said a silent prayer of thanks for his strength and courage, and that we were all safe and warm that night.

There is nothing mundane about winter on the prairies, then or now.

31

The Night My Brother Brought Down the House

Hallowe'en is scarcely over, but the Christmas decorations are up in the local department stores; by mid-November their aisles ring with carols. That means a busy and frenzied holiday season is at hand and we are coaxed into early participation.

Sometimes I choose to reflect upon Christmases past and, in particular, the simple joy generated by the country school concerts of years ago. That annual event was the highlight of the season in our rural community – especially during the Great Depression and the years of drought.

One special concert was most memorable for the chaos created by my younger brother. We all had parts in the concert that year; even the eight year old brother, whom we called PJ, was moved from the back row of the choir to a small speaking part in the "Christmas Story According to Luke."

PJ proudly brought home his part of the script written on a piece of scribbler paper as dictated by our teacher Miss Jones. It was one sentence long. Mother helped him memorize it and soon he was rattling off the words: "And there were in the same country shepherds abiding in the fields, keeping watch over their flocks by night." We heard him reciting it often, even as he did the chores, and yelling it loud and clear as he gathered firewood. He spoke the sentence without a hitch at rehearsals.

Finally the exciting evening arrived. Slicked down and shiny as we could be in our hand-me-down clothes, we gathered around the makeshift stage at the front of the room. The curtains drawn across the stage were made by pinning flour sack sheets to a wire strung from wall to wall. *God Save the King* was sung and the concert began, moving along in a reasonably ordered manner.

Moneca (centre) and brothers on harness horse at Grandparent's farm

Mother said later she felt a sense of unease as soon as she saw PJ standing on the stage. The curtains had been pulled back to reveal three young children down on all fours covered with white woolly blankets, and an older boy draped in his father's bath robe on centre stage. PJ stood stiffly off to one side, his eyes very wide as he stared at the sea of faces before him.

Now was his big moment, the time for him to say his one line. The audience was silent, waiting, but no sound came from PJ as he stood there, seemingly mesmerized.

"And there were in the same country..." Miss Jones whispered from the side.

Still no sound, no movement from PJ.

"And there were ..." Miss Jones said again, louder this time and with a touch of exasperation in her voice.

After another failed attempt to activate my young brother, she stepped onto the stage and read his line. Then she took his hand to lead him off. But he did not want to go! He grabbed for the curtain.

A wire anchor pulled out of the wall and the curtain came swirling down around actors and spectators alike. Noise and confusion reigned. The sheep hastily left the stage. Miss Jones and those at the front disentangled themselves from the sheets and wire, and PJ crept off to a safe spot beside Mother in the audience.

Half a dozen young men rushed to the front to help our pretty Miss Jones and in a short time order was restored. The sheep returned to the stage and the show went on without my young brother's participation.

The shame of his performance laid heavily upon PJ, and it was not eased until Santa arrived at the end of the concert and he, making no judgment as to one's acting ability, gave each child a small gift, a bag of candy and a big smile.

On the way home Mother and Dad assured PJ he would do better next time; he would learn, they said. Indeed he did. He grew up to be an articulate and effective speaker of some renown.

32

Eaton's

Now that the Eaton's chain has closed its doors, a post-mortem is in order, or at least the casting up of some personal memories about an institution that had been on the national scene for 131 years. To me, Eaton's is part of our heritage, a great contributor to the development of our country. My parents and grandparents dealt with the company. In 1918, my Granddad had even considered buying – from the Eaton's catalogue – the makings for a seven-room house for $999. Instead, he built his own, room by room, as the funds became available.

We had two important books in our prairie farm home – the Bible and the Eaton's catalogue. With no disrespect for the former, the catalogue definitely received the most attention. We mused and dreamed about the wonderful items on each page. The catalogue was our window on the world and it was well-worn and dog-eared by the time the new one arrived every six months, all glossy and colourful.

When Mother made out an order to Eaton's, we all tried for input, but, especially in those drought and depression years, she was very frugal in her choices. Two weeks later, the order arrived at our village post office, via the weekly train, and when Dad brought it home, we could hardly wait to open it. The parcel was wrapped in heavy brown paper and tied with a strong cord, both useful items in their own right.

Ordering from Eaton's catalogue was how we did all our non-grocery shopping. I don't know how the homesteaders would have managed otherwise as many farm families did not have a car and the nearest big town was fifteen to twenty miles away.

One time, Dad ordered a black and chrome heater for the upstairs and a radio. The heater warmed our bedrooms, but the radio brought magic into our home. On winter evenings, when the reception was best, we listened to wavering music from afar and the Amos and Andy comedy show.

The famous Eaton's Beauty Doll was displayed in every Fall and Winter catalogue and Santa brought me one when I was five or six years old. It cost $3.50, was two feet tall and sturdy, and thus survived my "mothering" to serve a similar purpose for my younger sisters. Years later, when we lived in Hamilton, my children had their own "distinctly Eaton's" toy: Pumpkin Head, a teddy bear with a patch of yellow "hair" on top of his head.

Changing mores in the marketplace resulted in discontinued publication of the catalogue. The last one was published in 1976 and our switch of allegiance to the Simpson's-Sears catalogue, a relative new-comer, was at first, half-hearted.

Eaton's brought pleasure and joy to the Christmas season and, when my children were small, figured prominently in our holiday preparations. The store was magnificently decorated for the season, and resonated with carols, the bells of Sally Ann ladies and Santa's hearty laugh as each child whispered his or her Christmas wish to him. The decorated windows were works of art, beckoning all to stop on a snowy street to admire a seasonal scene made with animated costumed figures, lights and music. My children loved them. We all did.

The best of all was the annual Santa Claus Christmas parade, an exciting and thrilling event for the children. Each year, as thousands of families did, we piled into the car and drove to Toronto and, armed with blankets and hot drinks, lined up along the streets to watch a wonderful mile-and-a-half-long show. There were marching bands and numerous floats: the Ice Princess, the elves, Santa and his eight reindeer – all of them showering the magic and joy of the season upon the wide-eyed children, and the adults too. The last parade was held in 1981, 77 years after the first one. It was the last major parade in North America to be fully owned, built and presented by one company. Perhaps its cancellation was a sad portent of things to come.

Eaton's was more than a commercial enterprise; it was a Canadian institution representing quality, community and family. Like my friend Ann, who worked there for 33 years, I am saddened by its demise and ignoble end. It can no longer "be my store."

33

The Green Velvet Album

The other day I was going through some boxes in the storage room, looking for the Christmas decorations, when I came upon the old green velvet-covered photograph album I had inherited a number of years ago. It had belonged to my grandmother and she had prized it greatly; it was the link to her past and to family in the old country. For years it had rested on the top of the dresser in her bedroom and we children were warned never to touch it. Decades later, after passing from one relative to another, the album, now rather battered, is in my possession.

The thick heavy pages have oval and square cutouts. Some of the openings were empty when I got the album but other openings housed professional photos of handsome and well-groomed men and women. I can only guess at their linkage to me – those men in suits with wide white-collared shirts and the women with smooth faces and dark eyes, sober in high-necked dresses with small adornments. A couple of current family members bear a slight resemblance, I think, to these distant ancestors. I wish I knew more about them. But I am glad to call them kin.

The grandmother who owned the album was the matriarch of the family when I was growing up. She had left Sweden when she was a young girl of sixteen and journeyed by herself to the United States. She married my grandfather Lars and, in time, they moved with their five children from Minnesota to Saskatchewan to homestead on the wide prairie. There were innumerable hardships and much strenuous work. When Grandfather died, she operated the farm during the drought and Depression years living there with her daughter, my Aunt Helgie, on the original homestead, two miles from our place.

One day, between Christmas and New Years, I went to visit them, taking along a small gift. I stayed overnight and that was a real treat for me, at nine years of age, to be away from home by myself. When the temperature that bitterly cold day dropped even lower, Grandmother suggested I sleep with her instead of on the small cot in the spare bedroom. I was glad about that.

Her room, one of four bedrooms upstairs in the big house, was furnished simply with a chair, a dark wooden dresser and a big high bed piled even higher with quilts and blankets. Resting on the dresser was the green velvet album, fastened shut with a lock.

Bedtime came early. After the kerosene lamp was blown out, I climbed up onto the bed and settled down beside Grandmother, my head deep in the thick feather pillow, the quilts pulled up to my chin. The bedroom door was open to any draft of warm air drifting up from the kitchen. There was no wind outside to stir the stark black trees at the window's edge; the land was locked in a frozen white silence. A pale moon shone in through the window and emboldened the dark shadows in the corners, but warm and cozy in Grandmother's bed, I was indifferent to them and to the creaking sounds on the stairway as the old house settled for the night.

That was a memorable Christmas and the last one Grandmother spent on the farm. She and Aunt Helgie moved into a small house in a nearby town. I never slept over again; it would not have been the same. Furthermore, due to lack of space, Grandmother's big bed was replaced with the small cot. There was barely room for the wooden dresser upon which the green velvet album had again been placed. It rested there until her death and, over time, found its way to our house. I am glad to have something to remind me of my Swedish grandmother and the album is now our symbolic link to the past and to those mysterious ancestors.

34

Electricity Lit Up our Lives

The warm sunny months are my favourite time of the year. I relish the long sunlit hours, even the rainy days, and I venture that everyone living in our northern climate shares this sentiment.

For children growing up on a prairie farm, springtime to autumn's end was the time for frenzied activities: attending fields and gardens, enjoying picnics and ball games, and warm evenings at the lake. But the short days and the long, dark, winter nights around the winter solstice, were often dreary and depressing. Before the arrival of electricity, we had to contend with that situation and "light" our way the best we could.

It wasn't easy. Darkness pressed down and around our farmyard in the late afternoon and dissolved all form, muted all sound, and intensified our sense of isolation. There was not a single light to be seen in the entire valley. The kerosene lamp we used barely held back the black night lurking outside the kitchen window, much less sent a beam of assurance to a lonely neighbour.

On December 21st, with a ring of relief in her voice, Mother reminded us that we had reached the shortest day in the year. The long, dark nights weren't exactly frightening or fraught with a sense of foreboding, but after the winter solstice we happily noted the steady lengthening of each day. Every minute counted.

It was, in part, our curiosity and, in part, our yearning for a life lived under an electric light standard or post that prompted my sister and me to ride by horseback on summer evenings to the top of the hills south of our farm. From that high point, at twilight time when the weather was right, we saw in the distance the lights of three or four villages, strung out like a glittering necklace laid across the land. Placed along the railroad tracks, about eight miles apart, the villages were peopled by those who had come west generations before. Observing that distant tableau, my sister and I mused about the folks who had gathered together to live in those little villages. It was the bright lights, though, that enticed us and triggered our imaginations.

Electricity came to our rural area in the early 1950s. We watched the hydro poles march across the wheat fields and into farmyards, bringing an exciting new dimension to our lives. Dad had two poles in his yard and I think he was always amazed at how, with a flip of a switch, the yard was bathed in bright light, illuminating the cattle huddled beside the barn, the feed bins, and the twisting path to the chicken coop. In the evening, the countryside was dotted with barnyard lights and even kitchen lights were bright and bold enough to flash across fields to the neighbours.

Old implements, such as the gas-powered washing machine, the battery-powered radio, and the kerosene lamp were discarded or, more likely, stored away for possible future use by those who learned frugality during the Depression.

The myriad of new machines and tools made work easier, of course, but it was the bright lights available when the sun didn't shine that had the most positive effect on the family. The electric lights pushed back the darkness of winter nights and gave us a sense of freedom and control. The feeling of isolation eased – and, finally, we had our own light standard to saunter under. Though artificial light cannot upstage the real thing, it does complement it very well, especially if you remember a time when the light pole wasn't there.

35

The Special Stable

Winter on the farm many years ago, when I was a child, was a relatively quiet and restful season. However, chores still had to be done and attached to that job was a curious and mysterious ritual my father performed each evening. The offhand reply he gave of "just the chores" when queried, seemed suspiciously vague and so I was determined to know more about it.

At nine o'clock every dark and cold prairie evening, Dad got ready to go outside. "Well, it is time," he would say to Mother in a hushed voice.

I heard him make the usual preparations as I lay awake in the little bedroom off the kitchen – the clang of the coffee cup as he set it down, the muffled sound of clothes and boots being put on, the screech of the lantern as he raised the chimney to light it and then the door closing behind him. I would try to stay awake until he came back into the house, stomping the snow off his boots and whistling a tune through his teeth.

Moneca and Dad, *ca.* 1928

Finally, when I was ten years old, and after much nagging, I was allowed to go out with him. That evening I sat at the kitchen table counting the minutes to nine o'clock, and a new adventure! The other children were asleep; only I, as the eldest, was permitted this passage into the adult world. I wondered what danger lurked outside in the inky black night, when the northern lights crackled and shifted across the sky and over the little barn wherein our animals sheltered. Now, I would discover what Dad did on his perilous night-time treks.

We stepped out into the cold night. The sanctuary of the house was left behind as we walked towards the barn somewhere in the darkness ahead. The only sound was the crunching of snow under our boots. I knew the land was vast and quite empty and, when cloaked in darkness, it was frightening to me. I looked up and saw the immense star-

The City Slicker Chicken and other tales

studded sky pressing down around us and I followed close behind Dad to keep well within the circle of yellow lantern light.

As we entered the stable, every head turned to greet us. The old horses blew a soft whinny. The cows whisked their tails, stepping from side to side, and the young heifer, big with calf, jostled for more room. The barnyard cat dropped from the rafters to my feet and, as I stroked him, his lean body vibrated with loud purring.

Dad opened the back door to the feedlot, and frosty air scented with the sweet smell of hay drifted in. He carried in the feed and there was much shuffling around as it was deposited in the mangers. The brown horse reached over and gently nudged Dad with her velvet nose, pushing his cap awry. The little barn, filled with the life energy of the animals, was warm and peaceful and the yellow light from the lantern added to the mellow atmosphere. Dad tossed forks of faded straw behind the stalls. The cat rubbed against my pant legs. I thought then about Mary and Joseph and how, so many years ago, they must have been happy in their special stable.

With the chores done, it was time to leave that little community. But we lingered a bit. Dad, fixing a halter, leaned against the broad flank of a horse while I sat on the milk stool and wondered aloud about how well our animals were looked after.

"They wouldn't make it through the winter without us, eh Dad?" I said.

"Right," he replied, "nor would we without them."

When he closed the barn door, darkness again gathered around and followed us up the path to the house. As we walked into the kitchen stomping the snow off our boots, Dad was whistling through his teeth and I tried to do the same.

36

Neighbour Remembered as a Hero

The Laft Hus is one of the buildings which have been gathered in Heritage Square, Red Deer, in a sort of museum of past structures. It is a well-appointed replica of a traditional Norwegian house. Partly in homage to my distant ancestors and partly because of the famed "goodies" sold there, I took my grandsons down one evening, a week before Christmas. We enjoyed the hot spiced apple cider, rosettes, and shortbread, which we ate around the fireplace, all the while being treated to a bit of folklore dispensed by a gracious hostess.

The Laft Hus is built of logs and the roof is covered with sod. A partial loft inside, under the roof timbers, and reached by a ladder, is the sleeping area. It is much like the homes in the Norwegian countryside, we were told.

And I know that is so. When I was a child on the farm, one of our neighbours was an immigrant from Norway who built his house in much the same style. However, the outside walls in Alak's small house were in concrete half way up in lieu of logs, and the top part was finished with wood. The roof, with its wide overhang, had wooden shingles. We thought the place looked strange, certainly different from other farm homes in our area.

Alak's barnyard, surrounded by a windbreak of young trees, was standard with regular buildings arranged around a windmill.

Like his house, Alak was also different, and that uniqueness enriched our rather staid community. He was a big man with a head of shaggy blond hair which he cut himself. He liked to read, and in that cash-strapped Depression era, actually bought books. According to my grandmother, books were a waste of time and money.

Alak often went to visit my grandparents, walking the four miles in good weather or skiing there in the winter when the snow was deep and windswept. At first the purpose was to "call on" my unmarried aunt, but when she spurned his attention, he continued to visit for different reasons. Over a good meal, or a game of whist in the lamp-lit kitchen, he and Granddad had long and comfortable conversations in their native tongue. Although I didn't understand, I listened to them, enjoying the lilt and cadence of their speech and the soft laughter over some private joke. Sometimes he brought along his violin and played a bit of Mozart after dinner. He also did that a few times at barn dances, much to the bewilderment of the dancers.

Alak spoke English quite well but he was anxious to read and write the language better, and so when there was no farming to be done he went to school with us. He squeezed into a desk at the back of the room, where he listened, read and learned.

Our strange neighbor is remembered especially for an heroic deed. He was credited with saving the life of a child one cold winter in the midst of the Depression. That week, in January, the Peterson's youngest child fell deathly ill. Our valley, already snowbound, had received another two feet of snow the previous week. The roads were impassable; horses floundered in snow up to their bellies.

The town doctor managed to send the essential medicine along the main road to a home – still eight miles from the Petersons. Alak, who was their neighbor, skied the sixteen mile round trip, in minus thirty degrees Fahrenheit weather and brought the medicine, carried safely inside his parka, to the grateful Petersons. The child recovered and Alak's frostbitten feet healed. He scoffed at being considered a hero, but thereafter, whenever he played a bit of Mozart at a dance, everyone applauded.

Some years later, perhaps because of the drought, or the winters or the loneliness, Alak sold his animals, gave away the chickens and left his farm. He returned to his homeland where he married and found employment teaching English at a university.

37

Past Memories Bring Added Pleasure

My New Year celebrations have changed a great deal over the passing years. I now generally welcome the arrival of another year quietly with a few friends. As is often the case at our age, such a gathering evokes memories of past celebrations – memories that run the gamut from happy parties to sad times spent alone, to bedside vigils with a feverish child, to times spent in exotic places, and to poignant and sentimental reminiscences of childhood events.

When we were young, Mother told us that half the joy in achievement is in the memory it makes. She is right; we fondly gather those past remembrances and add others as we greet a new year each January.

As a young child I was deprived of New Year celebrations. I was nine or ten years old before I realized December 31 and January 1 were days to be marked, as there was no overt observation of these at our farm home. Perhaps it was because we celebrated Christmas with such vigour, exhaustion decreed no further festivities until Valentine's Day in February.

When I was ten years old, I thought we should deal with this glaring omission and acknowledge the arrival of the new year in some way. Mother agreed to sit up with me and both of us, sleepy and bleary-eyed, watched the clock as the hands moved so slowly towards the magic hour. When I went to bed shortly after twelve o'clock I was dismayed, even traumatized; there had been no shooting stars, no flashing lights at the stroke of midnight.

Another year, my young sister and I banged pots and pans and yelled "Happy New Year" at midnight. Other family members, already asleep by that hour, did not respond favourably to our enthusiasm; neither did the dogs and farm animals who were also asleep in warm barns and sheds. But once aroused, all joined in and we had a cornucopia of sound to welcome that new year.

The next year, we donned our parkas and went outside at midnight where we heard the ringing of bells and the wail of sirens from the nearest town fifteen miles away, drifting through the still, frozen, December-January night. We wished we were part of those festivities.

Later, when Dad bought our first radio, we gathered around it at midnight and listened to the wavering, majestic sounds of the New Year's Eve celebration coming from Toronto with Mart Kenny and his Western Gentlemen playing *Auld Lang Syne*. We felt, though, that we were always on the fringe of these salutations to the coming year. Years later, when I was actually present at that New Year's ball in Toronto and saw and heard Mart Kenny play *Auld Lang Syne*, I thought then of those little girls on the lonely prairie farm long ago.

38

The Telephone System Isn't What It Used To Be

Modern communication boggles the mind. My son has a cellular phone, an elaborate machine with flashing lights in his home, a fax line, and an ostentatious apparatus in his car, all designed to put him in touch with anyone in the world in a few seconds. Now add the computer and e-mail to that mix.

This is high tech, I am told, but none of it can hold a candle to the wonderful old telephone machines and telephone systems of long ago, certainly not if one considers the social aspect and the down-to-earth, hands-on involvement of those early systems.

In the region of the prairies where I grew up in western Saskatchewan, the telephone company was owned by the local residents. As everyone had a vested interest in it, they co-operated to ensure the system ran as efficiently and economically as possible. For instance, young boys were strongly discouraged from shooting at the green insulators atop the poles, which were to my brother, for one, enticing targets.

Farmers, like my father, took care that the telephone poles with their crossbeams and humming wires remained upright and intact as they marched single file along roadways or across wheat fields and over the horizon.

The telephone mechanism was enclosed in a handsomely-crafted wooden box, about the size of a bread box, with a mouthpiece in the center, a receiver attached to a cord on one side, and a crank for ringing on the other. Securely fastened to an outside wall, usually in the living room, the telephone was connected to the wires strung into the yard from the main road.

Generally there were about fifteen families on each circuit or party line, and every home was assigned a number. Our number was "two ring three" that is, two long rings and three short rings produced by using the crank in the proper manner.

Although a particular ring was meant to call its owner to the phone, it was also heard in every residence along the line, causing a rush to most phones for the purpose of eavesdropping. That was called "rubbering" and although no one admitted to doing so, it was a common occurrence on party lines. Occasionally a person who was rubbering could not resist blurting out a correction, or adding new information, and then a three-way conversation ensued. Perhaps others would also join in and make it truly a party line. Modern day conference calls have nothing on this.

In the case of an emergency, such as a fire, one long furious ring would alert the entire community. The central operator was often able to provide additional information, such as the nature or location of the fire and thus help the neighbours deal with the problem.

In our area, the heart of the system, the telephone office was located in a nearby town in a small grey building on Main street. The false facade had one big window with a sign in it and the door from the street opened directly into a small anteroom.

Customers could speak to the operator working on the other side of a half door. The anteroom also had a solidly-built telephone booth where one could place a call and converse in considerable privacy – for as long as the oxygen lasted in that airtight booth!

Mr. Purdy, who serviced the miles of lines, was very dedicated. Like the postman, neither rain nor wind nor winter blizzards kept him from doing his duty and, if need be, he would scale a pole in a snowstorm to attach a wire and restore service.

That telephone system, primitive by today's standard, served many needs in the community. One cold and snowy February, Granddad suffered a stroke and he was lovingly and carefully taken to the nearest hospital, fifteen miles away. Unable to visit him because of the cold and the difficult snowbound roads, Grandmother was grateful to be informed daily of his condition. One snowy late afternoon, the phone brought sad news – Granddad had died. She hung up the receiver and for a long time stared out the window at the gathering night. How and when, I wonder, would such crucial information have reached us without the telephone?

My aunt was a telephone operator. Sometimes she would open the half door and allow me to enter her realm. That was where all the action was. I would sit quietly and watch her work. Sitting very upright on her stool in front of the switchboard, she whipped around the steel-tipped cords with great agility, plunging them in and out of different sockets, flipping buttons and keys and all the time saying "Num-bar poo-leez" through her nose. Ordinarily she did not speak that way, but that was her professional voice and she certainly impressed me.

The fact that Auntie worked there seemed reason enough for me to imply to my peers that we owned the place and maybe even all the telephone poles in the area.

Telephone service has changed considerably over the years. But, as I said to my son, the one with all the fancy equipment, I think telephone communication was more fun, and more challenging in the "olden" days.

39

Clothesline

On my way downtown the other day I saw a most uncommon sight. I pulled my car over to the curb at 116 Street to have a good look, but impatient drivers hurrying by on busy roads made me move on. Was I the only one who appreciated such a wonderful sight, reminiscent of a bygone era?

The object of my attention was an outdoor clothesline! It was strung across a backyard, from a post at the door to a big poplar tree. And even more impressive, a row of laundry hung the entire length of it. I was pleased to see that the clothes were pegged in an ordered and segregated way: the long white underwear together, then the coloured towels and pillow cases, tea towels and other smaller items. Where can you see such a sight in this day of clothes dryers and commercial cleaners?

The importance that washday once had in the household routine has been greatly diminished; it is no longer a significant event involving all members of the family. Now, laundry is a closet affair, never discussed, never thought about. Today an armful of dirty clothes, dumped into an automatic washer, is cleaned while dinner is being prepared. A half hour later it is moved to the dryer, and the laundry is done.

Contrast that with the washdays of yore. When I was a child, washing clothes took an entire day, usually Monday. It was a big job. Water was pumped, carried into the house and heated on the stove. The clothes were cleaned by either rubbing them on a scrub board or agitating them in a primitive, manually-operated machine. The kitchen, where the washing was done, was hot and steamy; meals were hastily prepared and eaten on the run. But when the clothesline was filled with clean laundry it was a rewarding sight – the sheets and towels billowed in the fresh breeze.

Even in the dead of winter, Mother hung the white wash outside on the clothesline. Each Monday there were rows of towels, sheets, flour sack tea towels (the sunshine bleaching out "Robin Hood"), and pairs of long white one-piece underwear fastened to the line, all frozen solid. Mom said some of the moisture was "frozen out" that way, but final drying of the clothes had to be done in the house.

In the late evening Mom went outside and pried the wash from the clothesline. From my bed in the room adjoining the kitchen I watched her march the stiffly frozen long underwear into the kitchen. She attached each pair with pegs to a line strung from wall to wall. In the dim light a white underwear suit stood rigid and menacing near my bedroom doorway, legs astride and arms outstretched. As the heat in the kitchen did its magic, the arms began to move slowly towards me, and then fall resignedly to its side. Only when the entire garment hung limply from its pegs did I close my eyes and fall asleep.

Apart from the occasional traumatic experience, doing laundry years ago was just plain hard work, often challenging, even adventurous at times. A return to those methods is not recommended, but that was the way it was done by our pioneer ancestors over the centuries. Maybe the folks on 116 Street are doing their bit to remind us of our past.

Reflection

40

In Pursuit of the Perfect Hairdo

"Do you ever marcel hair?" I asked Lyla, my hair dresser, last week as she fussed with my hair. It was definitely in need of her expert touch.

"Marcel?" she said, "what on earth is that?"

"It is a style, a way of curling hair that was used years ago. I believe it was very popular," I replied.

"Never heard of it," Lyla said in such a dismissive manner it had me mentally questioning my facts.

When I got home I looked the word up in the dictionary. "Marcel," it said there, "to dress the hair in even, continuous waves by means of special irons." When Mother and my aunts were trying to accomplish that feat at the dawn of history, my history, they were into style.

I remember marcelling being an issue of some importance among the women in our household, even though by then, that particular style may have been passé in the fashion capitals of the country. Because of geography and poor media we were always a litte behind in such important matters. Aunt Bertie, who was in Grade 12 that year, was heavy into marcelling. When she lost the special iron, she improvised, carving deep and sharp waves into her blond hair using bobby pins, and these dried into shape as she did chores around the farm. I don't know if she impressed the local swains. She did impress me.

But time moved on and the method of curling, styling, twisting, and bending hair changed. The next method, as I remember, was done with a simple curling iron. It was a scissor-like tool, different from the rectangular shaped one used for marcelling. Sometimes it was jokingly referred to as a branding iron for the hot iron could burn or singe hair, scalp, or an ear. But generally, turning the hair around the iron was done with great care to avoid such calamities. It was heated by placing it on a hot stove or, more often, it was carefully inserted into the top of the glass chimney on a lighted kerosene lamp. Grandmother did not approve of that risky procedure, concerned not for the hair but for the chimney. More than one was sacrificed to the pursuit of vanity. Today a sophisticated electric version is in common use.

My hairstyle was simple then: straight with bangs cut across my forehead. When I started school it was curled for special events. Between a multitude of duties, Mother found time to put my hair up in rags. That was a tedious procedure for both of us. I held one end of an eight inch strip of cloth on the top of my head while she wound a piece of hair around it and then tied the two ends together. These knots of hair and cloth bobbed on my head and interfered with my sleep. In the morning they were unwound and the rags saved for future applications. My hair was supposed to look like Shirley Temple's golden ringlets, but it never quite turned out that way. Nevertheless, I felt quite lovely with my head of fuzzy curls.

After the war, an enterprising young woman from up the line brought her waving machine to our village and set it up in one of the homes. It was a large apparatus that stood behind the chair where I, the customer, sat. Numerous heavy cords reached down from it like tentacles and clasped onto my hair. Captive, I sat there for the allotted time while the rods on the end of the cords heated up and strange smells emanated from the

Moneca, 7 or 8 years

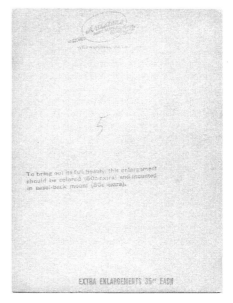

The back of the photo reads:

"Artistone Photo Service
Wetaskiwin, Alberta

To bring out its full beauty, this
enlargement should be colored
(50¢ extra) and mounted in easel-back
mount (30¢ extra).

Extra enlargement 35¢ each"

process. Finally, when the rods were removed, I was relieved to see that my hair had not vaporized. It was transformed into tight little curls that required a year's growth to undo. Soon a more refined version of that waving machine attracted lots of customers to the small Beauty Shoppe on Main Street in the nearest town.

Hard on the heels of that revolution came the home permanent. We bought the makings at the drug store, and then cajoled a relative or neighbour into spending part of an afternoon to roll and dab and rinse. We had the curls we wanted and saved a trip to town. Sometimes the outcome of this do-it-yourself venture was less than desirable, such as the time Mother's hair was made crisp and many colours lighter than normal.

The drought and Depression years presented new challenges to everyone. Mother and my aunts had to improvise new methods and solutions for their beauty regime. And that they did with ingenuity and humour. I don't think I could rise to such a challenge; I am happy to put my crowning glory in the capable hands of Lyla who is well versed in modern hair care. Besides, who needs a marcel anyway?

41

The Grand Commotion in the Big Sky

Recently I heard on the radio that Saskatchewan has adopted a new motto for their province, which I understand will appear on the new automobile license plates. The appropriate government department conducted a contest and a lady from Tisdale won the prize. Her entry was "Land of the Living Sky." Although I'm sure that decision was made with much forethought and deliberation, it seems like a strange choice to me. How can an inert natural element be referred to as "living," even metaphorically?

When I was growing up on a prairie farm, the big sky was always in our face, stretched as it was from horizon to horizon, attached only to edges of brown earth. It figured prominently in our day-to-day lives, as did the other natural elements that surrounded our home.

My family and grandparents lived on a section of flat land that provided a meagre living, depending on the whims of nature. Our little house and barn, set down on the vast land, clung like prairie grass to the earth. Some windy nights I feared the house might blow away, like a Russian thistle, or be swallowed up by the wide world lurking outside the kitchen door.

A keen awareness of nature came early and easily to the children of the prairie. I developed a love/hate relationship with the countryside and, in particular, with our big sky. It was the source of constant wonderment and apprehension, and was actually grander that anything on the flat, treeless ground.

I remember we were always aware of the clouds. Uninhibited by hills or woods, they drifted around at our fingertips or piled high like mountains on distant horizons. In summertime, I watched cloud-shadows on the grasslands or the grand commotion in the sky when a storm was brewing.

Often at the end of a hot summer day, towering black thunderheads, streaked with lightning, loomed in the western sky. Then we hurriedly urged the brood hen and her unruly chicks to shelter and tethered the new calf in the barn. "This will turn the milk sour again," Mother sighed as a clap of thunder broke overhead.

In the springtime, a grey canopy of rain clouds might sit snugly on all horizons for days on end – not a happy situation if one were claustrophobic as Aunt Bertie was. She was uneasy in small confining places, including the sturdy backhouse, and that feeling was compounded by heavy, overcast skies. Sometimes, then, I had to accompany her on her jaunts to the outback. Fortunately, over time, that fear vanished, even on cloudy days.

At times, winter skies were fiercely blue and cloudless and we were enticed out to play or to carry our skates to a frozen slough. Frequently though, snow-laden clouds blurred the horizon and we lived, anchorless, in a grey-white world.

The sky told tales of coming weather changes to those wise enough to heed the signs. For instance, a red sky at sunset promised wind and a certain tilt to the new moon meant rain. "That is a wet moon," Granddad would say, eyeing the heavens at dusk. There were hailstorms and blizzards, and the dreadful dust storms, after which the smell of dust hung in the air for days. I remember the night sky, star-studded, or often swept with shifting, crackling northern lights. Beautiful sunsets, sundogs, flocks of honking geese – the sky has it all!

These aspects that so impressed me when I was a child are, of course, evident today. My adult vision became jaded and blurred as I moved around the country and city skylines and lofty mountains filled my view. But the fact remains: the sky domain is a powerful living force. Forget the thought of metaphor. The lady from Tisdale has it right.

Moneca Wilson

*No matter how far you get from home,
it always pulls you back.*

I guess that's because you carry it around inside you.

Moneca Wilson

Moneca Wilson was born in a small town in southwestern Saskatchewan during a time when life was simple and communities and families were closely-knit. Times were difficult at first. She and her parents lived with her dad's folks in what she fondly remembers as the Big White House. Her grandparents had been pioneers in the area. They started with the traditional sod house and built from there. Like the other people in the area, they farmed the land.

Then came the years of drought. Her family moved to a farm adjacent to her grandfather's property. It straddled the Alberta-Saskatchewan border and became the scene for many bittersweet experiences during those years. She spent a number of her school years in the small prairie town and some years later a vacation to Ontario turned into a twenty year odyssey. She married and had three children.

Moneca's roots in the west ran deep and she came home to be near her family. She's retired now and spends time in community activities and with her writing.